Contents

FICTION

Vacuum   5
James Kelman

Blin   61
Uilleam Blacker

Ship of Fools   66
Fred Johnston

Russian Blue   102
Regi Claire

Civil Rights   122
Catherine Czerkawska

POETRY
Ross Wilson   10
Dorothy Lawrenson   23
Ian McDonough   45
Bernard Pearson   119

ARTICLES
Scots Pine   17
Andrew Greig

Home Thoughts From Abroad   26
Robyn Marsack

Chosen Route   33
Jen Hadfield Interviewed by Jennie Renton

Banking Meltdown   36
Kenny Kemp

The Common Breath   48
Tom Leonard

A Dislocated Life: Flora MacDonald   III
Hannah Adcock

Homecoming 2009   128
Will Brady

PHOTOGRAPHS
Robin Gillanders—Highland Journey   77

REVIEWS   135
Hannah Adcock
Ross Alloway
David Borthwick
Tam Dalyell
Alasdair Gillon
Andy Gloege
Stephen Lackaye
Michael Lister
Murdo Macdonald
Ian Macwhirter
Colin Nicholson
Dilys Rose
Julius Ruiz

Edinburgh Review 126

Passing Place

Edinburgh Review

EDITOR: Brian McCabe
ASSISTANT EDITOR & PRODUCTION: Jennie Renton
REVIEWS EDITOR: Michael Lister
ADDITIONAL ASSISTANCE FROM: Fiona Allen, Julia Boll, Aiko Harman, Patricia McCaw, and Ryan Van Winkle

Published by Edinburgh Review
22a Buccleuch Place, Edinburgh EH8 9LN
edinburgh.review@ed.ac.uk
www.edinburghreview.org.uk

ADVISORY BOARD:
Robert Alan Jamieson, Gavin Miller,
Colin Nicholson, Faith Pullin, Randall Stevenson
Edinburgh Review 126
ISBN 978-0-9555745-7-3
ISSN 02676672

© the contributors, 2009
Printed and bound in the UK
by Bell & Bain Ltd, Glasgow

Individual subscriptions (3 issues annually) £17 / $27 / €27
Institutional subscriptions (3 issues annually) £34 / $54 / €54
You can subscribe online at www.edinburghreview.org.uk
or send a cheque to *Edinburgh Review*
22a Buccleuch Place, Edinburgh, EH8 9LN
Back Issues are available at £5.00 each.

Edinburgh Review
is supported by
Scottish
Arts Council

Edinburgh Review is a partner magazine with eurozine www.eurozine.com

James Kelman

Vacuum

She was moving around. She would be tidying. She did this to keep up her spirits. Thump thump. No she did not, she did it to make me feel guilty. one thing was for sure, there was no need to tidy. Nobody ever visited the place. How come she had to tidy? How come she kept on tidying? Morning noon and night it drove me mad. The girls never visited, nobody visited. The last people to visit were neighbours with a burst pipe who shouted about water coming through their ceiling. It had not come through any ceiling, it came down through the light. The water followed the track of the wire: electrical wire. They failed to notice. Stupidity. They were lucky they had not short-circuited the entire block of flats. That was a month ago. The wife did the talking, she was good at that kind of stuff. I could not look at them. Except for the postman that was the last visitors. We had sons. They never came. When was the last time? I could not remember. A month ago at least. They had their own lives of course. Of course.

This tidying and dish washing drove me up the wall; counter cleaning, washing machines, mopping the linoleum, polishing the bloody ornaments and hoovers hoovers hoovers. What a din! That is what it was, a pandemonium, if you were trying to read so you needed to concentrate. I tried to concentrate. It was not easy. Nothing was easy. Not nowadays; it was hard reading at all without her to contend with. I determined to ignore it, including the sound of her moving, she would move, would always move. She done it to irritate me. She said she did it to make me aware of reality. That was the way she put it, as though reality had given me the slip. She could get on with life roundabout, the daily grind, unlike myself; this is what she implied. Oh, I said, okay, right, of course, you're so much more at home in the world than I am. Excuse me. It is so obviously the case why bother talking about it? So obvious I forgot.

No answer.

The front door was ajar. I pushed it further open, enough to shout through: What exactly is this reality you keeping talking about? Just tell me, I am very interested to hear. Do you know something the rest of us dont?

She did not answer. She knew a trap when she heard it; I would have something up my sleeve. If she replied she would have been finished, I would have got her. I would have had something lined up to say, and I would have said it. She was cornered, I had her. She knew it now, if not already.

But it wearied me. I retreated to the kitchen and shut the door, sat down at the table. I closed my eyes. I opened them. It was true: I was trying to get her cornered. That is what I was doing Looking for ways to attack. It was quite bad, even perhaps despicable, if you were describing it.

It was our lives. This is what it had come to. And it was me responsible. She was not doing it. I was. I needed to straighten myself out. It was not her it was me.

But I was at a low ebb. I knew it and so did she. Both of us. It applied to our relationship as a whole. Alhough it was me especially. I accept that. I would never have denied it. There was something up with me and I could not get myself out of it. I tried but could not. I needed to and I wanted to, if only I could and I would, if she would help, if only she would, and she could. She had it in her power.

Oh but she had such faith in my mental strength! So she said. Not in so many words. It was all unspoken with her.

My mental strength! Some hopes. My mental strength had gone. Did I have any to begin with? She thought I did. She thought I would sort out myself, because I sorted out everything else. She was being sarcastic.

But I could have, and I would have. Of course I would have. As long as I knew what it was. Then I would deal with it. You have to know the situation. She spoke about reality but that was reality. If you were unaware of the situation then you could not deal with it. She could have helped but she did not. Even to let me think, if she had let me think, let me think and I would work it out. She did not let me think. All this tidying and cleaning nonsense. How could you think! Washing and bloody polishing. It should have been reminders she was giving me, not all this racket racket racket. That was a pure attack. It was help I needed and she attacked me.

I needed help to handle the situation. It was not only for my sake. It was the two of us. We would both suffer. Did she want us to suffer? Maybe she did, she hated me that much. Else why attack the person closest to you? This is what she was doing. Why would you attack the person closest to you? It is a contradiction. Maybe I was not the person closest to her at all, maybe it was somebody else. At our age! Why not? Why not at our age? In this world anything is possible. People and things we regard as immoveable, they are not; things change and so do people, your soul mate turns out to be something else.

But I knew that was not how it was, I knew it was not, it was only how she did things and got it into her head, if she would just not get things in her head.

There was no sound now.

Of course not. She had been at it all morning and needed a rest, she would want a cup of tea, and could not get one. She could not get one because I was here, in the kitchen, so she could not come in and put on a kettle of water. What a situation. I got up from the table and opened the door, and went ben the front room. The hoover was there but she was not.

She was in the bedroom, sitting on the bed. She looked up, surprised to see me. I smiled. Why attack me? I said. I'm the person closest to you in this whole rotten world.

I dont think it's a rotten world.

Well I do.

I dont.

My world's rotten.

Well dont drag me into it, she said. She did not look at me when she spoke. I preferred her to look. I was looking at her. She knew I was. Just dont drag me into it, she said.

I'm not going to.

Then dont.

I waited a moment. Now she glanced at me. I knew she would. I just knew she would. I dont want to drag you into anything, I said, and I wish I didnt have to.

Well you dont have to. You dont have to at all. You dont. Go away and drag somebody else. Why are you smiling?

Who me?

Why are you smiling?

I'm not smiling, I said, except at this point I did smile. It was unfair and I knew it was unfair. Blatantly unfair. Yet still I did it. Sometimes I have a thing in me; I know that I am a man. We both do. She is weaker, as a woman. It is just a physical thing. I have the physical strength. I have it in me. She is so much weaker. I could just hit her. I could. I would not like to say what I could do to her. She was staring at me. She did not know what I was thinking. It was inside my head. She did not know what went on. I was glad she did not. I needed her not to. People need their space and their privacy, me too. Sometimes she looked at me. I did not like how she did it.

But it was my fault. It was. I knew it was. If she would just help me, why did she not? I wished she would. I honestly did. But she did not even talk, she did not talk, why did she not talk it drove me actual mad, just straight angry mad that was what she did and she did not have to, she just did it. Did she even know I had her cornered? Of course she did but what did she do about it? Nothing. I wanted to scream. She reached for a pillow; why I do not know. I do not know why. What was a pillow going to do, a piece of flimsy cotton or wool or some stuff. She did not speak. Why did she not speak? That aggravated me. She did aggravate me, she had it in her power and she used that power. She had her power. Women do. She did.

She was looking at me but then was not, just at the carpet floor; if she needed to hoover, maybe she was wondering.

She knew how this would start. The very words that came out my mouth. It did not depress me. Her challenge on reality was the key. I had not replied openly. I pretended to mishear. We might have been watching television for all the difference it would have made. I brought it up out the blue and her heart sank. I was smiling. I was unable to stop myself. Even before saying it I was smiling. At the very idea! She would have been expecting it but not even knowing she was expecting it! Until I did it. Then she would. And she was beat. She knew she was beat. She knew I had beat her. She was cornered.

How had I managed it? It was so good I felt like writing it down for future situations. It was a beauty. I could have written it down on an old envelope if I had found one, also a pen, if I could find one of them. But we did not keep them in the bedroom. Bedrooms were not there for that purpose. Envelopes and pens were for the living room writing-cabinet just like cups and saucers were for the kitchen and vacuum cleaners the walk-in lobby cupboard.

I had no interest in any of that. The present was difficult enough. Concentration was the key. I would apply the brains, would have to, get the grey matter moving.

Or so I thought. Only for a moment or two. Who was kidding who? As if I would manage that. It was what it was. As far as I was concerned anyway. Although what was it? One wondered. Even the way she was looking at me. How come she was looking at me? So I looked at her. I stared at her. It was not hard to do.

Ross Wilson

Anither Season

In memory of Alex 'Spangles' Hunter (1936–1995)

When they found Marciano's body
strapped in the crashed plane seat,
someone said, Start counting, he'll get up.
He always did, when he was down.

I remembered that story the day
Spangles went down.

A sweet tooth behind a bark:
thir'll be no fuckin' swearin in this gym!
A face marked by 626 fights.
At 59, he went down refereeing a bout
with no one to replace him to take up a count
that went by so fast we had our doubts
it was over.

That's anithir season yeh've wastit!
He'd say when I'd return to the gym
years after my last fight,
and with more appetite
for the atmosphere than the blows
that carved and cut and shaped him
like a pumpkin fired within.

Anithir season wastit
as though he thought I'd be back.
As though to say: he's just resting.
I was young after all.

Now, I hit harder with the weight
time packs into a punch, and slower,
with energy that saps like the sweat
I watch drip away, wondering
what Spangles would say
about this new club full of women
and bairns and music – attitudes
shaped by the seasons he's been gone.

His voice plays on – an old record
scratched and scored as his face,
and turning in my memory:
This isnae a fuckin' youth club!
As if to say: this isn't a game.
You don't *play* boxing.

Months after the old club
was knocked down and out of existence
the headline read:
Final Round for Boxing Legend.

That was 1995.
This is another century, another gym
with the same fighting spirit alive
in twelve-year-olds I watch spar
and prepare fir anithir season.

The ABC

Wee Barry was first – his first bout.
Three rounds with a twelve year old double.
    Mirror images until
The glass shattered like a dream
    And reality battered his wee face red.
    Barry cried in the changing room:
Ma nose hurts like hell!
    Only a point in it, Alec said,
        Ye done well.

Then there was Sean.
    Features ghosted with nerves,
    Sean flushed vomit and
Minutes later, seconds out, was hit out
    Of time. A wee one asked: *did it hurt?*
        No! The pain
Was several inches south of the blow.
    Sean didn't bleed:
    Blood bloomed his cheeks.

Lanky Colin jabbed and crossed, dangling
    Danger on the end of two rods,
    A smug grin as each jab went in and in.
In the closing seconds a hook sank into
    His burger-Coke lined guts. Winded,
        He grappled a pummelling desperado until
The bell sounded, sweet as his girl the night before.
    Colin won by a score:
    Nineteen hits to four.

Next, John. A Scottish champion six years
    Before nightlife blackened his eyes
        Darker than any glove ever did.
Body hardened by Saughton's gym,
    Arms colourful as an exotic birds wings,
        Rage carried him into the ring, through two
Wild rounds into a third. Drained as a
    pint glass, a white towel fluttered
        To save him from himself.

Dean! Dean always broke the circle training –
    Facing a mirror as the rest faced one another.
        I-Pod in ear, unable to hear instruction,
Dean danced and vaulted the ropes!
    But a boot snagged and tumbled him.
        And laughter bellowed around the ring.
It was hell for Dean after that. Pride punctured,
    Body blows deflated the rest.
        And his record fell: four wins, now a loss.

Last: eighteen, unbeaten, Andy sat
    On a table staring at boots that run miles
        Every night they don't skip rope in a gym.
No one will fight him: *too much power, skill.*
    There are whispers of other countries;
    Talk of a blue vest.
'I've no passport,'
    He told Alec.
    'Your passport's talent 'n' will.'

Weekends Alec drives a transit van full
    Of bleeding noses, bruised ribs, battered egos.
    Sixty years old and so alive his breath
Is a winter plume against a darkened windscreen.
    Half way cross-country tonight.
    Tomorrow: a roof with hammer and slate.
Alec smiles into a mirror full of boys
    Sleepy with dreams or dreaming awake:
        the future is full of girls and fighting.

The ABC (2)

James came and turned
away from a right cross
in pain and walked across
 the street for a bottle.

Craig put on two stone of muscle,
boxed a guy naturally heavier than him
and discovered the truth in:
 there's nowhere lonelier than the ring.

Stewart had talent but lacked will,
won a few fights, missed nights
training, got a girl pregnant and
 no one knows where he went.

Graham went sixteen and two,
won a few district titles, a national,
boxed international and
 died inhaling aerosol.

Lisa was a tomboy lesbo bitch
according to a few people before
she learned to fight back and
 flattened Fat Mary on her back.

Alan wasn't very good – he got better,
lost a few before he won,
never won much but
 got there.

All six were in the same year.

James is on the dole now.
Craig is a bouncer.
No one knows where Stewart is.
Graham is in Kirkford Cemetery.
Lisa is at the university.

And Alan runs the local ABC
    three nights a week.

Andrew Greig

Scots Pine

When I go, I'd like my sign-off to be even briefer than Norman MacCaig's last goodnight to me: *Ta-ta*.

As the car hums over Drumochter in radiant late May, it is thanks I want to give again, despite everything. A lot has happened, some painful, some revelatory, in the years since Norman died, but through it all I knew this day had to come.

The back seat and car boot are stashed with big rucksack, maps, boots, carrier bags, waterproofs, tent, sleeping bag, stove, food, boxes of fishing gear. My rod is propped in the passenger seat. It twitches as I drive, my slender nodding passenger.

When I cleared the gear from the glory hole yesterday, the old lines and casts were inextricably tangled as my country's history. Nothing for it but cut off the lures worth keeping, make up new casts and throw out the bourach. Truth is I'm not much of a fisherman, an apprentice at best, and I haven't fished for ages. The friend who taught me how to, who should have been with me on this ploy, died on Everest, in his tent at Base Camp, a book across his chest.

I still wonder: which book? I'd been in Sheffield, at L.'s, when the call came from Joe Simpson. 'Andy? It's bad news…'

Mal Duff is gone. For nearly ten years he challenged my life, dragging me into Scottish winter climbing en route to three serious Himalayan expeditions on the Mustagh Tower, Everest North East Ridge and Lhotse Shar. In our times off the hills, he introduced me to his other passion: fly fishing. We fished together, not so many times that I can't remember each one of them, in lochs and reservoirs of the Lothians, the Borders and my childhood haunts near Bannockburn.

If I hadn't fished with Mal, I never would have mentioned it to Norman, for fishing to become our principal subject of conversation whenever we met, leading to me being here now, descending the A9 at speed past the signs to Culloden – let us put old defeats behind us for a while! – down towards Inverness, its glinting bridges and broad dolphin-torn estuary.

What is this love, this painful and absolute attachment I feel to Scotland? Why do these bare rising green-brown hills, these fields, this river, even the familiar cast of the houses, feel right and move me so? It baffles L. She accepts she is English but it's not a defining fact for her, any more than being right-handed or blue-eyed. Whereas she can see that for me being Scottish is fundamental. I cannot walk away from it.

As I turn off at the Tore roundabout onto the A835 to Ullapool, drive on past those low scattered villages where the broad valley wedges apart the hills on either side, I'm thinking of one of MacCaig's shortest poems, 'Patriot'. *My only country/ is six feet high/and whether I love it or not/ I'll die/ for its independence.*

The idea of patriotism was abhorrent to him. He'd seen enough of what it led to. He could not love an abstraction. But he loved – my God how he loved! – things that were solid, particular: some people, dogs, frogs, rivers, mountains, toads, a wild rose bush, so many kinds of birds. His vision was earthly.

That last evening at Norman's, we had been talking about fishing in Assynt. He flicked his thumb over a tiny badge on the lapel of his tweed jacket. *AAA.*

'Nothing to do with motorcars or alcoholics,' he said dryly. 'This is the honour of which I am most proud.'

'More than the OBE?'

He giggled, the air hissing through his teeth. MacCaig was lucky, his brain was good to the end. But in his last years it was as though the old man moved aside at times to let the child he'd once been peek out at you. It was in the giggle, the love of childhood expressions like *ta-ta*.

'Much more than the OBE. Some people whose good opinion I cherish made me an honorary life member of the Assynt Anglers Association.'

But his legs – circulatory and heart problems, acerbated by constant smoking – had become so bad he could no longer fish in his favourite lochs, hadn't been able to for years now. He lapsed into silence, sipped his whisky. His face had sunk, leaving the jutting cheekbones, high eye-sockets arched over the watchful, mournful, lustrous eyes. Maybe it was his Gaelic inheritance, but Norman could drink whisky and talk all night. Now he looked lost. Since his wife Isabel died five years earlier, these silences came more often.

Maybe that was why I asked, in one of those confidences that come after midnight with drink taken, just the two of us in high-backed armchairs near the fire, 'Norman, what is your favourite spot in the world?'

'Assynt,' he said. How much love and memory he loaded into that one word.

'I know it's Assynt!' I said. 'But *where* in Assynt? Your favourite place?'

He took his time. Another drink, another drag of the fag.

'I think it would be *the Loch of the Green Corrie*. Only it's not called that. AK and I used to fish there.' His head turned and fixed on a small black and white photo that was always on his mantelpiece. An eager-looking man stands outside a church somewhere; in dark suit and tie, hands on hips, grinning at the camera with an air of brimming mischief: A.K. McLeod, mourned in simple, desolate poems. 'It's many years since I've been there. It's remote, you see, high up in the hills and quite a scramble. I think about it a lot.'

And that was when he laid the charge that has brought me here. 'In fact, I should like you to go and fish there for me.'

He leaned forward and tapped me on the knee.

'I loved that man!' he said vehemently.

I drive through Garve, then the junction where one road goes off to Achnasheen and the red-ledged towers of Torridon, the hills of Kishorn. Roll those words around in your mouth as though they were whisky. These names, these places, have histories for me, starting with childhood holidays, my father's husky voice telling stories as his gloved hands turned the big wheel of our Humber Hawk.

This is about how emotion and history accrete, layer upon layer. James Hutton, leading citizen of the Edinburgh Enlightenment, identified the geological cycle that made our planet and makes it still: Erosion, Sedimentation, Metamorphosis, Uplift, further Erosion. This account may not be so much about fishing as about how, in our very short-lived way, we are eroded and transformed.

Straight on up Strath Garve, my heart rises with the road. The landscape has emptied out, as though someone had pulled a historical plug from a great bath – someone did – and now any house or car is an event, the hills all-surrounding, the river flashing brown and clear over stones. I wind the window down to check the air: moist mild sweetness with underlying bitter acidity. I have entered the West.

Off the road to the left, on a lee slope below the burn, I notice a solitary Scots Pine. Some are drawn to the rowan, the mountain ash with its blood red beads simmering through drizzle. The oak, silver birch, copper beech, all are noble and useful and have their adherents. The Scots Pine is mine.

On impulse I stop and get out of my useful mobile cage, walk across the moor to that tree. I run my palm over the rough red-brown plates of its bark, lean in to sniff its resinous heart. I look up at the blasted, twisted branches, snapped, stunted, some clearly dead, the others still passing energy into that enduring core.

My brother the forester talks of the 'expression' of tree species. Each has its own encoded shape, the way it will grow, its final height, even its natural life span. All very determinist. But he showed me how that shape is affected by circumstance: a plantation of Scots pine, close-planted, all stand thin and slim and straight, very good for telegraph poles. That shape is in response to proximity. Whereas my image of the archetypal Scots Pine is like this one: stumpy, twisted, with big horizontals. Enduring, blasted, thrawn, solitary…

The very image of my father, who first named it for me. He was not good at trees, nor very interested in them, but this one he named as something special, as though it mattered to him.

I sit down at the base of the tree, lean my back against it and look down the glaciated, deserted valley. Indubitably and mysteriously, Norman MacCaig was significant to me. Some people signify in our lives, even though we do not see them often, and we may mean little to them. Urbane, subtle, caustic, he was an intimidating, welcoming man alert with laughter and increasingly with sorrow and loss. Had Norman been a tree, in his latter years, after the death of A.K. Mcleod and then his wife, he would have been an elegant, lightning-struck silver birch. That last evening we had together, he looked ancient, lost, devastated. And then the quip, the giggle. *'You've heard that one before? Well, I am in my anecdotage!'* Hissing giggle. *'And have I said that before?'*

But now I'm leaning against something of my real father. He is at my back, as he always is since he died some twenty years ago. It is he I have to make a reckoning with, that powerful, difficult, armoured man, so shaped by his circumstances – the two World Wars, his drive and his sensitivity to slights, his friends who died young, his early poverty and dead loves. With my old man you could see the snapped branches, the broken crown, the force of his endurance.

Then I have it, that scrap of story I had sensed stirring in my brain that made me stop here.

It began as a yarn about how he and his classmates, in the early years of the last century, would challenge each other to walk as long as possible carrying a penny gripped between thumb and forefinger, the arm hanging down. *'It may seem an easy thing to do, laddie, but no matter how hard you try, sooner or later it will fall from your grasp.'* Muscular fatigue, numbness, something like that. And I thought, what a fantastically futile thing to do, and how deep and Scottish a teaching it must have been, yoking together money, willpower, and the inevitability of loss.

Then my father went on to say how once, still carrying his penny, he stopped in a gale under a Scots Pine. He stood against it, thrilled – not a word he had much use for – to feel the trunk shift against his back. He said he'd imagined the tree a mast, and yearned to be sailing where that wind was blowing, far from narrow Arbroath, out of his dreich country, beyond tired Europe, to a blue space on his father's globe. *'The South China Seas. I was aye minded to go there.'*

And in his twenties, he did. Penang, Sumatra, Borneo, Java, he knew them, lived and worked and loved there. If not for a woman, I think he would have stayed. Exile would have suited him, as it suited his five older brothers who also fled their dreary, stifling, impoverished country, my Scotland.

Early on during that last evening I spent alone with him, Norman fumbled in the pocket of his jacket. 'I need you to help me,' he announced.

He produced a hearing aid. I leaned over him and fumbled to fit the earpiece. He sat patiently, staring straight ahead. I had to hold his ear away with one hand to work the clip in behind it. Handshakes apart, I had never touched Norman in my life. It was unsettling to feel his old, warm, soft ear-skin between my fingers.

He sat back. 'That's better. Now we can have a proper conversation – though I expect I'll say the same old things.'

I sit watching the flare of light over the distant Deargs to the West. *The poet's ear*, I think. *I could do with that.* MacCaig's high cheekbones had swollen to primitive arrowheads lodged just under the skin. His skull had been warm against the back of my fingers.

There had been something dreadful in his patience, his passivity as he'd sat looking ahead while I fumbled with his hearing aid, like Larkin taking off his bicycle clips 'with awkward reverence'. Norman in his pomp never asked for help, any more than he would have shared private emotion. Now loss, weakness and age had reduced him to this raw self. I had thought *reduced*, but I wonder now if *raised* or *freed* might be more it. Sometimes he saw it so. 'I have a long streak of reticence in me,' he'd announce, 'and now it's being worn away.'

He had already spoken warmly of his health care visitor – '*a nice-looking woman, very kind*' – and his son's and grand-daughter's visits. Easy to see it as humiliating, such dependency admitted, the warm food brought by a helpful stranger doing her job, the acquaintance fumbling with your ear, yet it may be that in its necessity and our acceptance of it, we are ennobled as much as reduced, and in that stripping bare life is truly revealed, frightful and radiant.

I am not my father, nor Norman MacCaig. Sitting under that Scots Pine off the road to Ullapool, I know my business is not to carry money till it drops, and my scheme is not one of exile from this place. The bittersweet myrtle-laden breeze out of the West passes over my face and arms, but I do not yearn to follow where it is going. My predilection would be to locate my own Scots Pine, then sit against it listening until I know the place the wind is coming from, and live there, if only for the few last seconds.

Dorothy Lawrenson

Stretching Paper

The prologue is the part I linger over,
finding reassurance in its small familiar drama
– stretching the paper.

Full-blast, the cold tap whirlpools the bath.
Immaculate, each sheet requires immersion
in its cold profundity.

Innocent against off-white enamel
the paper's purity admits of no desire
to play support to a creative act.

Good paper is set in its ways, knows its own identity:
rough, hot-pressed or not, acid-free, mould-made,
it loves stability, is consistent as its own weight.

Stretched on a board, it bucks in protest,
buckling as it dries. Its defeat is predictable;
minute by minute, the waves subside.

Minutes apart, I suffer each little victory,
counting the white indictment of every square
as, one by one, they lie back down again.

Leaving Fife

Kingdom of Leven, Ladybank and Leuchars;
you are to me like some eccentric uncle,
with your strange suggestive hills,
your round ravilious fields,
and that black hole left by coal at your heart.
With those pretty edges you look like a doily
for the cities to rest their long spoons.
Paunch above the central belt,
fat with fields of yellow rape,
links and scores,
pig-farms, pantiled cottages,
small stranded villages,
Pit-this and Kil-that.
Your modesty exceeds Dundee's;
your tourist board's logo is the high road south.
What can I say? I'll follow the lead
of a Crusoe, a painter, a millionaire,
and – in this order – love you, and leave you.

Making Headway

It was one of those days – I could tell from the dead drinks,
remnants of pints massed in a Gormleyesque field
at his end of the bar. 'How's life?' I braced myself.

'Life? It's like a bloody line-dance:
two steps forward, two steps back.

Life is a hair shirt, socks and pants,
and at night, hair pyjamas.

It's taking the Odessa Steps by threes
on your hands and knees,

or carrying all your dreams in a colander
just to watch them pour out like tears.

At last the House suggests your departure
when you've no chips left to cash in.'

I heard him out till he bought a round
then changed the subject, recalling the Caley Mac ferry
that took us from Wemyss Bay to Rothesay;

the gull that was neck-and-neck with us all the way over,
translating us into his element, seeming to hover

six feet above the deck, static on the airwaves
holding himself steady, gradually making headway.

Robyn Marsack

Home Thoughts From Abroad

I spent much of last year in New Zealand; that is, my inner life was going on there. I was reading dozens of collections by New Zealand poets, as co-editor of the anthology *Twenty Contemporary New Zealand Poets* that has recently been published in both the UK (by Carcanet Press) and NZ. It's an odd feeling, being so absorbed by one culture while living in another, and in this case thinking also of how to 'sell' one culture to another. My co-editor, the poet Andrew Johnston, has lived in France for a decade, so we both know a lot about the insider/outsider identities of transplanted adults. Yet it was also a very familiar feeling, that mixing of inner and outer worlds and the contradictions that come with it. In the dark days of the Scottish winter, approaching my late-January birthday, somehow I still expect sunshine. In New Zealand, it would be edging towards the beginning of the school year, therefore the best weather.

If I think of those childhood summer days, I don't think first of afternoons at the beach – though there were plenty of those. I see myself, in shorts and a top or a sundress made by my mother, sitting on the brick steps of our porch. Or half-in, half-out of the front door, its great slab of grooved black wood holding the sun's heat, the paint a little blistered by it. Somewhere in the background there might be a radio, broadcasting the racing commentary delivered at top speed, or the slow-paced cricket. There are lines of ants trekking from the pot-plants on their stand across to the nirvana of the flower-beds, over the hot bricks – the same procession that was to transfix my two-year-old daughter decades later. And I am reading.

Of course I did other things as a child: played hopscotch (after a lot of practice) or gyrated with my hula hoop (ditto); ineptly joined in the Saturday afternoon tennis enjoyed by the rest of the family; went to ballet classes; played endlessly with dolls or paper-dolls; went to the beach but never learnt how to swim. My most constant occupation, the unfailing joy, was reading.

What I read had very little to do with my surroundings: a douce suburb of the capital city in the apparently placid 1950s and '60s; buffeted by the wind but in my memory becalmed in summer. At the end of our street were the Botanic Gardens: beautiful native bush and birdsong. One or two banks would be alive with glow-worms after dark – if you approached them quietly, and let the night settle about you. Beyond those were the lush Lady Norwood rose gardens: whoever she was, the roses growing about her name were – are – gorgeous. And between the bush and the roses were the main lawn and the Sound Shell, built the year I was born, where bands played on Sunday afternoons. Sometimes there were pipe bands with their accompanying Scottish country dancers. Now I think of it, the gardens on a Sunday were our equivalent of Kelvingrove: every sort and kind of family strolling amidst the flowers and foliage with a keen civic pride and sense of ownership, much like those strolling past the stuffed animals and Colourist canvases in Glasgow. The Dominion Museum in Wellington had – in my memory at least – no such crowds or pride, as visitors squeaked across its acres of brown, institutional lino to reach the Maori meeting-house. It never occurred to me that the building's name indicated a certain cultural status, a dependency. It sounded grand.

Even now, that disjunction between my experience and my reading seems natural. My reading was almost entirely about 'home', and that place was not New Zealand. It was, essentially, England. Despite the dancing – my mother and I were amateur Scottish country dancers ourselves, in the winter, in our church hall; both of us small and light-footed, whirled around by large men in kilts – and the bagpipes, and the Scottish songs we sang in the car, I don't think that Scotland made a deep impression: that was more of a South Island inheritance. My mother and aunt, living at the foot of the North Island, were raised to think of England, where their paternal relations lived, as 'home'. Things were sent out to them from home: the long-awaited velvet pinafores, for example: brown – a lasting disappointment to my mother; she had been so set on black. There were dolls; replicas of things made for Queen Mary's dolls' house, of which I inherited the tiny jar of strawberry jam, still sealed and bright; some books, too. Rose Fyleman's *The Fairy Flute* has survived – she was the author of the song 'There are fairies at the bottom of my garden', which my mother used to quote (and also, I have discovered, of the unfortunately titled 'The Fairies Never have a Penny to Spend'); and the book I loved, *The Mary Frances Story Book* by Jane Eayre Fryer: 'adventures among the story people', who believed in 'truth and beauty, and courage and kindness', as one might long to in 1923, with the Great War only five years past.

Yet I know now that the pioneering *School Journal* was flourishing as I was reading such books, with a stated mission 'to provide "reading material" for children who inherit New Zealand as well as western civilisation'. What a fabulously confident statement! In 1951 J.C. Beaglehole, the foremost historian of his day, praised the *Journal* for making children feel

> that life in New Zealand can be a worthwhile and interesting experience, that New Zealand has a tradition and contemporary ways of living of its own; that New Zealanders are doing fascinating and important things here and now, that can best be written about and drawn by New Zealanders.[1]

Mine was the generation that received through school the famous – or infamous – *Washday at the Pa*: a simple text with photographs of real people by Ans Westra, a Dutch-born photographer.[2] What a stushie that caused! It was withdrawn from circulation after Maori and Pakeha protests. I am sure that my grandfather saw my copy and raised his eyebrow. Neither the argument nor the *School Journal* – in which I might have read work by Janet Frame, for example – was central to my imaginative life.

Instead I was reading the books my contemporaries in England were reading: Lorna Hill's novels about Sadler's Wells, for example, and Noel Streatfield's *Ballet Shoes*. Re-reading that, years later, I was struck by the emphasis on money, on straitened circumstances, on make do and mend. It had chimed with my own family situation. At about 10 or 11 I discovered the marvellous world of historical novels, English again: Rosemary Sutcliffe, Elizabeth Goudge; Henry Treece, Geoffrey Trease and Ronald Welch. Of course there were the North American classics, too, with their train of sequels: *Anne of Green Gables*, *What Katy Did*; above all, *Little Women*. In all this, there was nothing that spoke to me of my life in Wellington: summer in January, Easter in autumn; no hint of snow except on the distant Kaikouras across the Cook Strait, on a very clear day. There were no Maori or Indian children -- though these were exotic in my own school, like the Canadian girl with a *divorced* mother; nothing seemed newly built – everyone in those books was so settled, even the Elizabethans, perhaps especially the Elizabethans. No earthquakes or kowhai or possums.

In a 1964 *School Journal*, the same year as *Washday* made its brief appearance, Margaret Mahy published a poem which addressed exactly that disjunction I recognise:

Our Christmas Day is blue and gold,
And warm our Christmas night. [...]
We know our Christmas by these signs
And yet around my wall
On Christmas cards the holly gleams
And snow flakes coldly fall,
And robins I have never seen
Pipe out a Christmas call.[3]

Hers wasn't a name I knew then. Katherine Mansfield, I think, with 'The Garden Party' and 'The Doll's House', was the first New Zealand writer to make an impression. Moreover, she had been at my secondary school. Other New Zealand writers followed, and indeed the father of my schoolfriend Katie actually was a writer; but those early voracious reading years were basically filled with English images. It was perhaps no more curious that my head should be filled with English history than that boys growing up in Barrhead and Renfrew and Dundee should be reading Jennings and Billy Bunter and *Just William*. I read *William*, too, in my brother's red-bound copies. Their public schools and home counties life were as far from the Scottish streets as from ours in Wellington.

There are two sublime pleasures of reading: recognition and escape. If I was denied the pleasures of physical recognition, the pleasure of escape – the intense pleasure of total absorption in a different history – was everywhere available. Of course I agree that children should experience the sense of confirmation that comes from finding in the pages of a book the landscape – physical or emotional – that is familiar to them. Equally, we need to escape that familiarity and live elsewhere. We want, like Max in the *Where the Wild Things Are*, to venture through the unknown and still find our tea waiting for us, hot, at the end of the day. Some days we want to migrate without packing our bags.

When I settled in Britain, I needed an easy answer for people who asked about my migration: why was it, when New Zealand was so beautiful and life there – as they simplistically understood it – was like Britain in the 1950s, did I want to stay in the UK? If you grow up preferring books to beaches, and art galleries to outdoor pursuits, then naturally you will gravitate here, I'd say. It was shorthand but it carried some truth in the 1970s, and it confirmed the old country's sense of cultural superiority.

It was an answer that wouldn't do now. Although I'd arrived by plane, the whole business of flying between hemispheres was only just becoming affordable: that two-day journey, long enough, was in recent experience four weeks or more by ship. Katie's family had done that: I remember seeing them off at the wharf, with streamers and the traditional singing of 'Now is the hour/when we must say goodbye...' People could be gone for months and years, saving up for the return. Sometimes they didn't return. They communicated by letter. Telephone was for emergencies; telegrams for special occasions. All those English magazines we read from cover to cover – from *Princess* and *Judy* to *Woman and Home* and *Women's Own* – were shipped over, arriving at least three months out of season. Now the books and magazines are there simultaneously, the films earlier. The journey is still exhausting but the separation – the isolation – is not so complete.

If your native language, if not your accent, is the same as the country's to which you've migrated, and your understanding of its culture is fairly sophisticated – through that same reading – then the process of emigration/ immigration is blurred. The pain of changes, the frustrations, the absence of shared references, are not so immediately apparent. It seems that the migrant has to make scarcely any effort to be accepted, nor 'home' any effort at accommodation. Almost seamlessly, the pakeha New Zealander is absorbed by the host country. Of course, I wanted to be accepted. This was the society on whose literature I had been nourished for decades. It was a homecoming: winter in January, with those robins; Easter – appropriately, at last – in spring; the mesmerising fall of snow on city streets. Oxford's magnificent libraries and striped lawns; London's galleries and concert halls; eventually Glasgow and Edinburgh, architecturally rich and solid, culturally rich (although oddly, to the newcomer, still agonising over Scottish identity) – all this I embraced, cherished. This was the culture that stamped the New Zealand in which I grew up, whose approval meant everything. To be published or to exhibit or perform in *London*: that was the seal of arrival.[4]

That accent enables you to escape immediate class identification and limitation. In Scotland, it means that you escape 'English' identification and limitation. New Zealanders slip under the barrier of the expected: two New Zealand Gentiles were in charge of organising the opening exhibitions of the Jewish Museum in Berlin in 2001. One of them, Nigel Cox, in his fascinating posthumous collection of essays *Phone Home Berlin*, remarks of the New Zealanders that came to see the museum: 'I am floored by their worldliness, their informed alertness... Yes, under the towelling hats, beneath the any-old shirts, New Zealanders keep brains which are [so] accustomed to problem-solving, hearts that history has not broken...'[5] I was very struck by that characterisation when I first came across it. Having been immersed in history through all my reading, and loved the long-settled landscapes of Britain, I was yet unprepared for history's dragging weight, how it might function as a lock rather than a key. I should have understood, coming from a dominion, what it meant to have been governed from Westminster for 300 years: I understood better, ten years ago, when the Scottish parliament was resumed.

New Zealand has no close neighbours. Its inhabitants 'live at the edge of the universe', as Bill Manhire says in his poem 'Milky Way Bar', and what used to be a drawback can now be perceived differently. These days, I am lucky to know quite a few New Zealand poets, and it's poetry that sustains a vision of 'home' for me. I'm a New Zealander who has never watched a rugby match all the way through, and never live, but how I enjoyed *The Book of Fame*, Lloyd Jones's novel about the 1905 All-Black tour of the UK, and Anne Kennedy's rugby interlude in her narrative poem *The Time of the Giants*. I can carry New Zealand in my head in ways that, when I was younger, I didn't care about doing.

As children we're given a home, and as adults we have to construct one, which may be far from where we started out. It's the result of choices and chances. Reading, for me, is part of the construction. Sitting in the northern light of my kitchen in Glasgow, with the vast blossoming cherry-tree beneath it, showing that the longed-for spring has arrived and that the days will lengthen until there's almost no night, I look up from my book of New Zealand poetry and can hold these homes in their hard-won, shifting balance.

Notes

1. Quoted by Gregory O'Brien in A *Nest of Singing Birds: 100 Years of the New Zealand School Journal*, Wellington: Learning Media Ltd, 2007. Substitute 'Scotland' for 'New Zealand' and I think that this is what some Scottish educationalists are asking for now, so much later in this country's history that it seems astonishing to an outsider.

2. A *pa* is a Maori village, originally fortified, which varies in size from those constructed for a few families to a tribal settlement. One of the reasons for complaint was that the Maori family portrayed in the book in fact lived in a private house, not a *pa*. See the entry on the website http://tpo.tepapa.govt.nz for an outline of the controversy surrounding this school bulletin.

3. Quoted by Bill Manhire in his essay 'Christmas', *Doubtful Sounds; Essays and Interviews* (Wellington: Victoria University Press, 2000), where he makes a good case for 'the everyday pleasures of incongruity'.

4. And yet, seated right at the language gates, there were sentries from New Zealand, all Rhodes Scholars: Kenneth Sisam, who was Assistant Secretary then Secretary to the Delegates of Oxford University Press (1922–48); Dan Davin, Deputy Secretary to the Delegates (1948–78); Robert Burchfield, editor of the massive four-volume Supplement to the *Oxford English Dictionary* (1957–86). Burchfield also revised Fowler's *English Usage* and, according to his *Guardian* obituary, is 'positively thrilling on the distinction between shall and will'. It's not as simple as the empire striking back, but an element of that is there – we were nearly invisible, we were patronised, yet New Zealanders guarded, defined and extended the English language in its most formal incarnations. See the study by James McNeish, *Dance of the Peacocks: New Zealanders in exile in the time of Hitler and Mao Tse-Tung* Wellington: Random House, 2003). The use of the word 'exile' is interesting and debatable.

5. Nigel Cox, *Phone Home Berlin: Collected Non-fiction*, Wellington: Victoria University Press, 2007.

Previous winners of the T.S. Eliot Prize include Carol Ann Duffy, Seamus Heaney and Ted Hughes. The latest poet to join this stellar assembly is Jen Hadfield for her collection Nigh-No-Place, *which is rooted in the dual locations of Shetland, where she has lived for three years, and Canada, where she likes to spend time with her 100-year-old grandmother. Kathleen Jamie has called her 'a zestful poet of the road, a beat poet of the upper latitudes'. In 'Rogue Seeds', as Hadfield describes her artist books, elements such as wood, fish-flies, photographs, linocuts take root along with words in unexpected combinations. The empathy she has with the natural world brings depth and vitality to her individualistic ecopoetics.*

Chosen Route
Jen Hadfield interviewed by Jennie Renton

> *I go to the rockpool at the slack of the tide*
>
> *to mind me what my poetry's for.*   ('Daed-traa')

Were you a big reader during your childhood?
Not really, possibly because I found it very hard to sit still for very long. The stuff that was going on creatively for me was going on in my own head – I didn't play with other kids much, so my fantasy world was unbridled. I was brought up in Cheshire, in the suburbs, right on the brink of the country. What did light me up was exploring the fields and wild places near our house.

It seems the natural world is still important in lighting up your imagination.
Yes, and when it does happen, everything happens at once – I'll be reading, writing, drawing, having notions and making lists about what to do next, and then I'll be quite tired for a bit. I really like just sitting and looking at the land. The very first time I went to Shetland, where I live now, I didn't have a car and I was on my own most of the time – and I was totally overawed by the place that I found myself in. I spent a lot of time sitting on the doorstep,

looking, not knowing when I was going to stop sitting there. Something of that feeling has fed into my creative process. Recently I heard the term 'ecopoetics' and I thought, if the thing that I'm doing had a name, that would be it. But I'm not particularly swayed by movements, or what other people think, or whether they would say I'm part of a tradition or not; if my writing is in parallel to a tradition, it's accident rather than a chosen route. I'm always going to end up doing my own thing.

What motivates you to bring poetry out of silence?
I'm not sure I understand it but when the impulse is there, it's unmistakable. I'm always delighted when someone responds to something I've written, always surprised that I've reached other people through my poetry. But as someone who has been so self-isolated through life, I can't say that communication has been my main aim. All I know is, writing makes me feel like me, it's like a song that I need to hear. However much I question what right I might have to put my voice out into the world, the impulse to do so, when it comes, is compelling. And it's to do with naming, though not in the sense of defining. And wanting to praise the land, and the fact that I am here and have gratitude for it.

Writing from a sense of the sacred?
Absolutely. A sense of the sacred is something I come back to again and again – and don't often think original thoughts about…

Does anyone?
Oh, God knows! If I were a philosopher I'd probably take that a bit further, but I'm not: I'm a *sense* person. I frustrate myself all the time not following thoughts a little further, but what I'm talking about is sensory action, almost. And to do with sense of self.

Tell me more about that sensory action. Do you usually think in words?
It's more like tongue-tipness, I guess… sounds, speech rather than words… 'words' makes it feel like something written.

I once heard poetry described as being written on the breath.
That's the kind of thing: you will be walking along and you will be talking

to the landscape and praising it and telling it that you love it. I can't track down why I started doing it, except that I know that all my life I've had strong, compulsive attachments to places, often new places where I have no history. I remember as a kid going on holiday to South Wales and one dull day ending up on a hillside I desperately didn't want to leave; we'd been to gorgeous spots the days before, we went to lovely places the days afterwards – but that was *the place*, and I didn't want to leave. I felt at home there, and safe; but not just safe – exhilarated, lit up.

That notion of the potency of new places reminds me of Alistair MacLeod's No Great Mischief, *in which a Scottish migrant ejaculates on setting foot on Canadian soil, the new land.*
It's a funny thing, the significance I attach to being in new places. I'm scared of what will happen to me if I don't have that experience. I'm very comfortable living in Shetland, but regardless of where I'm based I need to get away regularly or I start to get into a rut. I have to take opportunities to go looking.

So you shake yourself up and rattle your poetic bones by placing yourself in a different landscape?
As much as anything, it makes sure I don't get narrow-minded. That's something really important to be careful about. As far as rattling the 'poetic bones', I'm fine-tuning what is needed for that. I've discovered simple, quite practical things: for instance, if I'm away from home, I find it very difficult staying anywhere that isn't self-catering because I hate being served; also, I need to be able to paint without worrying about someone's chintz bedspread.

You talk about taking yourself seriously as a writer, without forgetting to be playful, and of getting back to it after quite a long break; I can imagine that to get the accolade of the prestigious T.S. Eliot Prize might make all that more daunting, as well as being a potential spur.
Getting the T.S. Eliot Prize did make me anxious for some weeks but I'm used to anxiety, so that's OK. The fuss and press interest is only temporary; I'll have lots of time to think about the real issues. At the moment I'm just enjoying metabolising any expectation there may be and using the whole experience as a catalyst to get back to writing.

Kenny Kemp

Banking Meltdown

It is difficult to comprehend how and why Scotland's major banks collapsed so spectacularly. Many of us in the Scottish media covering their giddy rise to greatness and global strength over the past fifteen years were captivated by the almost miraculous ability of the bankers with the Midas touch. We had become cheerleaders for our national institutions, as they increased profits year upon year, but rationally, in the back of our minds, we knew something would have to give. And it did: with profound and massive consequences.

There were tell-tale signs that our bankers' behaviour was running out of control back in 2003 yet few, including the UK Government and the City regulators, paid any great heed to this. When I interviewed James Crosby, then the Chief Executive of Halifax Bank of Scotland, for the *Sunday Herald* that spring, I asked him about the UK's overheating property market and whether he feared a collapse. He assured me the fundamentals were secure and that we still didn't have enough homes in the UK, so he maintained that house prices wouldn't fall. He was wrong. Looking back, I think the people who ran our banks should have known much better and exercised greater caution – instead they were driven by the allure of a bonus culture which invited them to take more risk. Increasingly, the banking industry was seduced by 'innovative' financial derivatives and instruments that very few people actually understood. And the traditional Scottish banker who once had a reputation for prudence and thrift was swept along in this global current.

The collapse of Northern Rock in September 2007 was only the prelude to what was to come as the UK's banking system seized up. But no one could ever have predicted how bad the fall-out would be in Scotland. The twin pillars of Scotland's corporate power – the Halifax Bank of Scotland and the Royal Bank of Scotland – collapsed in September and October 2008, forcing one into a shotgun merger and both to be propped up by the UK taxpayer to the tune of billions of pounds. The ignominy will be felt by Scots for many years to come – and the question will be whether Edinburgh can ever recover its mantle as a leading international centre of financial excellence. The cost in terms of those thrown out of work, the lost income from corporate taxation and the UK's increasing burden of national debt will have a detrimental impact on every citizen of Britain. The only way out for those seeking to balance the nation's books is for public services to be cut back and for personal taxation to rise. That's a stark fact of life after the banking industry was allowed to run out of control because of lax financial regulation.

On Thursday 18 September 2008, Halifax Bank of Scotland was rescued from the brink of collapse in an emergency take-over by Lloyds TSB. Late into the previous evening the negotiations went on before HBOS was forced into a 'shotgun marriage' with Lloyds, with competition rules waived by the UK government. Scotland's First Minister Alex Salmond blamed the investment markets saying: 'We are basically in a position where a bunch of spivs, speculators and hedge funds and short sellers can effectively drive a bank merger.'

Mr Salmond, a former banking economist, was partly right. Halifax Bank of Scotland was the author of its own demise, allowing its investment and joint ventures in the sphere of corporate and commercial lending to spiral out of control. When the sub-prime mortgage crisis, which originated in the real estate hotspots of Florida and Las Vegas, caused paralysis in the important inter-bank lending markets, HBOS was doomed. A merger was the only viable option on the table, sanctioned by two Scots politicians, the Prime Minister Gordon Brown and the Chancellor of the Exchequer Alistair Darling. Between September and the following April, there were more dark days for Scotland as an unprecedented global meltdown battered small countries such as Ireland and Iceland and destroyed the Scottish Nationalist's aspirations of an independent nation in an 'arc of prosperity'.

On Monday 13 October 2008, the UK Government was forced to pump £37 billion into the recapitalisation of the country's major banks, including RBS and HBOS. Over the coming months the Chancellor of the Exchequer, HM Treasury and the Bank of England needed to intervene again with new measures to ensure the stability of the UK's economy. Amid the storm, the chairman of RBS, Sir Tom McKillop, and the Group Chief Executive Sir Fred Goodwin, were forced to step down and, at HBOS, its chairman Lord Stevenson and Chief Executive Andy Hornby were ousted.

By Friday 3 April 2009, there was still no certainty that all the strong medicine was working. This was the day of the Royal Bank of Scotland's annual general meeting in Edinburgh. More than 500 angry shareholders – whose investments were now worth pennies – turned out to hear how the new management of the Edinburgh-based bank was going to restore the fortunes of the once-mighty bank. The newly-installed chairman Philip Hampton, in explaining that the bank was posting losses of £7.9 billion and was writing-off £16.2 billion in goodwill after the disastrous bid for ABN AMRO, a Dutch bank, said: 'The past is done, we cannot change it. We must recognise what has happened and why, identify lessons and learn them.'

The past was far from done. Less than a week later Royal Bank announced it was cutting 9,000 more jobs around the world, after announcing 2,700 jobs would go from its 106,000 workforce in the UK.

At the annual meeting, a stream of small shareholders stood up to lambast the previous management and in particular, Sir Fred Goodwin, who had become by now a figure of hate and ridicule across the UK because of his refusal to accept a cut in his lucrative pension pot. As one irate shareholder told the meeting, those involved with the bank's demise should have gone to jail – not been paid millions in extra pension benefits. Goodwin – as 'Fred the Shred', a nickname he earned after cutting costs during his time at Clydesdale Bank – came to symbolise the nation's acute hatred for bankers – and Scottish bankers at that – even although Sir Fred held a Glasgow University law degree and a chartered accountancy qualification, rather than traditional banking exam certificates.

These traumatic events have been a severe blow to the Scottish financial psyche. There is anger and resentment that trusted banks appear to have thrown away some of the intrinsic values of traditional banking in pursuit of short-term glory and aggrandisement, and the pursuit of individual corporate bonuses. Of course, they are victims of the wider global meltdown which began in the United States, but why were the Scottish banks caught out while other more cautious banks have survived?

The soul-searching in Scotland has thrown up a fundamental question: is there any truth in the legend that Scottish bankers, by their nature, were more diligent, more frugal and more committed to the virtues of thrift and prudence? One of the illustrious commentators on Scottish banking was S.G. Checkland, the Professor of Economic History at Glasgow University, who wrote the seminal work, *Scottish Banking: A History, 1695–1973*, (Collins, 1975). He suggests there were circumstances which made Scots unique.

Checkland said:

> In the formative period of modern banking, before 1850, the Scottish system was a good deal more important than its absolute size would suggest, for it was more advanced relative to its economy than was the English, or indeed any other; qualitatively, it was in many ways more intensive and more progressive. Indeed, Scotland for several generations between 1740s and the 1850s held a unique place in world banking development.

The Scots pioneered many areas of banking, including the principle of limited liability; the adoption and issue of the bank note to the point where gold and silver disappeared; the system of the branch network; the development of deposits and the payment of interest; the early development of joint-stock banking; and the practice of a bank holding other banks' notes as security. And, relevant to the enlarged Lloyds Banking Group, which now include Bank of Scotland, Scotland also created the first savings bank in 1810 when the Reverend Henry Duncan, a Church of Scotland minister, opened his savings bank to help the poor in the parish of Ruthwell in Dumfriesshire. It was Duncan's local campaign against poverty and hunger which led him to explore the idea of savings for the labouring classes. This, in turn, spawned the Trustee Savings Bank movement, now subsumed in the Lloyds Banking Group. Other Scottish innovations along the way included the introduction of hire purchase; the notion of a non-banking holding company as a means of integrating a banking group; and the creation of a professional class of bankers. This cannot be underestimated. The term 'professional' in a business context imparts a degree of status, responsibilities and duties, and implies a set of qualifications and code of standards which all members must adhere to. Scotland set up the first Institute of Bankers and it exported its trained bankers – with their shared values – with many rising to the top of banks around the globe. Checkland said: 'These elements, taken together, placed the Scottish system in an outstanding position.' His work now desperately needs to be updated – with a proper academic examination of the following thirty-five years.

The Royal Bank of Scotland and Bank of Scotland shaped the nation's destiny. The Governor and Company of the Bank of Scotland, founded as a public bank established by an Act of the old Scottish Parliament, on 17 July 1695, was the cornerstone on which Scotland's banking system was laid. Scotland's reputation for parsimony was damaged by its failure in Panama and the fledgling Bank of Scotland faced an early crisis as the Darien Company tried to break the bank by seeking the redemption of its notes for cash. But it survived and prospered and over the next 300 years, Bank of Scotland would absorb over twenty other Scottish banks. The economic history of Scotland includes the Union Bank of Scotland, British Linen Bank, the Central Bank of Scotland, the Caledonian Bank, the Glasgow Union Banking Company, and a dozen other smaller names such as the Ship Bank and the Thistle Bank.

Henry Hamilton in his book, The Industrial Revolution in Scotland, (Cass, 1966) said the development of Scottish banking was 'intimately associated with the expansion of industry and commerce, and this close contact has been effected very largely by the peculiarly Scottish institution of cash credits.'

The new Bank of Scotland was granted two important privileges by the Act of Parliament: the monopoly of Scottish banking for twenty-one years and freedom for their joint stock 'from all publick burdens to be imposed upon money' for a like period. The statute also imposed on the bank the obligation to cash their notes in specie (for cash or gold).

But one innovation was the introduction of paper currency, which was backed by the bank's capital. This allowed the bank to expand credit and facilitate payments. Two types of bank note were issued, both valued in sterling. One was negotiable only at the point of issue and included the name of the payee – which was the forerunner of a cheque – the other was payable in cash on sight to a bearer who did not need to be named. This was the direct ancestor of the modern bank note.

When the bank's monopoly period was over the Privy Council in London rejected its continuation. The royalists proposed the establishment of an alternative. The arrival of the Royal Bank of Scotland in 1727 sparked a bitter 'bank war'. Some say this long-running rivalry was a characteristic of Scottish banking until 2008. The Royal Bank of Scotland was able to usher in this new era with the establishment of mutually dependent cash credit and deposit systems. Any reputable person, on the security of two or more people, could apply for a cash credit. This was immensely important for it allowed people of good character, with little or no security to secure advances on the bonds of more substantial people.

In essence, it placed value on the trust and integrity of individuals not to let down their bond-holders – and it encouraged industry so that banks could be paid back with interest. These became ingrained Scottish patterns of business behaviour – 'My Word is My Bond' – although, at times, it was subject to abuse and fraud. This was the basis for Scottish banking expansion and its international export of practitioners around the Empire. A Scottish banker's relationship with his borrower was built on a foundation of mutual trust.

As the new millennium began in 2000, Scotland's financial services sector never looked stronger or more confident. There was a definite buzz in the air about banking in Edinburgh and Glasgow. In September 1999, both Royal Bank and Bank of Scotland announced pre-tax profits of over £1billion for the first time and the life assurance business companies had declared record new business figures. The merger of Lloyds-TSB and Scottish Widows was just being digested and the amalgamated mutual brands were in better shape. In the fund management houses, the total amount of funds was nearing a peak and there was a steady flow of excellent deals for the corporate financiers and the venture capitalists. But the old ways of banking were disappearing, replaced by a new retail approach to selling services and short-term relationships that lasted only as long as it took to sign a deal.

Throughout the second half of the 1990s, the level of financial activity in Scotland had become unprecedented. Doom-mongers predicted the complete capitulation of the mutual industry forged over 180 years ago by the Scottish traditions in prudence and cautious investment. Yet many of mutuals had actually been mismanaged and their capital bases eroded. There was a spate of amalgamation aimed at Scottish mutual pension and life companies. Revered brands such as Scottish Amicable, Scottish Equitable, Scottish Life, Scottish Mutual and Scottish Provident were all bought out and this caused some consternation north of the Border. Yet the promise of fresh injections of capital led to Abbey National taking over Scottish Mutual in 1992 and then Scottish Provident in 2000; the Prudential taking over Scottish Amicable in 1996; the Dutch giant Aegon acquiring Scottish Equitable in 1998; and Royal London taking over Scottish Life in 2000. Standard Life stood alone as a mutual, until it too became a public listed company.

According to Scottish Financial Enterprise, funds managed by Scottish assurers, investment companies and banks increased nearly 20 per cent to £217.8 billion in the year up to December 1998, compared with £182.6 billion the previous year. By 30 June 1999, the total reached £232 billion – and expected to top £250 billion by the end of the year.

Gavin Gemmell, the then joint senior partner at Baillie Gifford, one of Edinburgh's most progressive fund management businesses, said: 'Some of the success is due to tradition and history. Life companies and investment trusts started a long time again. But there is also an open outlook in Scotland which attracts global investors.'

But as the New Year began, the battle for the National Westminster, sparked by Bank of Scotland, was still unresolved as both Scottish banks became embroiled in a major takeover battle of a larger English bank. This was a watershed in the growth of Scottish banking. Royal Bank's victory caused huge soul-searching at the Mound HQ of Bank of Scotland, which ultimately led to the merger with Halifax. In the pursuit of more profit, the Scottish banks forgot about the importance of their relationships. Bank balance sheets in the UK and the US grew much faster than household or corporate debt. There was an explosion of credit within the financial system and loans were increasingly 'securitised' and sold on to other institutions. There was a malaise also among the credit agencies which gave credibility to such investments – when in reality they were a crock of trouble. But another failing was the Labour Government's early decision in 1997 to create the Financial Services Authority and curtail the power of the Bank of England. This has now proven to have been a disastrous mistake which allowed bank expansion to go virtually unchecked.

By January 2005, the Royal Bank of Scotland, having brilliantly integrated NatWest, was flying high too as the sixth largest banking group in the world in terms of its market capitalisation. This was an outstanding achievement for a Scottish-based business. The Royal Bank's success had helped Edinburgh's financial services economy grow four times faster than the overall economy – and twice as fast as the entire UK sector. The new £350 million Gogarburn corporate HQ, which was on-time and on-budget, was preparing to welcome over 3,250 staff.

Over at HBOS, a management shakeup heralded the promotion of Andy Hornby, the 38-year-old head of retail banking, to chief operating officer preparing to succeed James Crosby. A former ASDA executive, Hornby had been a rising star at HBOS since joining in 1999. This shake-up in June 2005 also brought the retirement of George Mitchell, chief executive of the Bank of Scotland's corporate division, and his replacement by Peter Cummings, the corporate managing director, dubbed 'the Banker to the Stars'.

This was a significant step-up for Cummings who had started at Bank of Scotland at the age of fifteen. He had assisted some the UK's best-known entrepreneurs financing their deals and he provided debt for Philip Green's takeover of Sears, BHS and Arcadia. He had been a staunch supporter during Green's bid to win Marks & Spencer – but Cummings also pursued an expansionist policy of increasing debt to commercial operations. This worked well as markets rose higher and higher. It was indeed a golden age for Bank of Scotland's Corporate division – and there was an illusion that they were invincible. Any probing media inquiries about banking deals were met with derision and scorn. But the seeds were sown and this was the cause of the bank's eventual collapse when lending dried up and the valuation of property assets collapsed.

Yet still the banks pressed on. In August 2005, RBS announced that it would lead a team investing $3.1 billion to buy a 10 per cent stake in Bank of China. RBS was to put up $1.6 billion of its own cash. Investors were beginning to get a bit cagey about RBS's global aspirations. But there were signs that the market was becoming freaked out by Goodwin's Chinese adventure. Shares dropped as it was feared he would be risking too much of the bank's capital in a market in which it had little or no experience.

In Britain, tell-tale signs were beginning to appear over consumer debt levels. All the major banks, including Barclays, HBOS, HSBC and then Eric Daniels, the Chief Executive at Lloyds TSB, warned of rising levels of bad debt provision as higher interest rates impacted on UK consumers. Was this nothing to worry about – or a tiny indication of a potential seismic tremor? The irony was that banking analysts were critical of Lloyds' 'sluggish' performance as opposed to the more gung-ho approach of HBOS and RBS. Everywhere, the traditional Scottish values of prudence and caution were being underplayed.

In July 2005, Sir Tom McKillop announced he was stepping down as chief executive of AstraZeneca, the pharmaceutical group, and was immediately tipped to take over from Sir George Mathewson, as RBS Chairman. But there were also questions raised about his suitability as chairman of a major bank as he had no direct experience of financial services. There were raised eyebrows at the appointment of this Scot to the RBS board, although the businessman had helped transform Zeneca – an offshoot of ICI – and Swedish company, Astra, into a successful multinational business.

But it was Sir Fred's unbridled folly in leading a consortium in 2007 to take over the Dutch bank ABN AMRO that was the killer blow for RBS; his ultimate decision to trump Barclays and proceed with the take-over, paying a premium for the pleasure, earned him the sobriquet of 'The Worst Banker in the World.' In April 2009, the chairman said: 'With the benefit of hindsight it can now be seen as the wrong price, the wrong way to pay, at the wrong time and was simply the wrong deal.'

The Scottish media is having to tell a new story because banking in Scotland now faces a bleak future. More job losses will be announced and borrowers – be they personal or business customers – will find it harder to gain credit, set up a new business or find a home loan. In short, life will become very tough in the financial sector, and whether Scotland can bounce back and re-emerge with its traditional values and virtues intact remains to be seen.

Ian McDonough

Beginning to Learn Gaelic

I think of Wade and his road building Regiment,
bold as red robins, flattening our contours
like panel-beaters taming raw blooms of ore,
secreting ordered grammar as they strode.

These are the paths they taught me how to track –
surefooted till some relict
in my mind was roused. Now here I am,
stumbling over strange yet half-familiar gaps.

A spate of aural memory floods back –
my Mother's split tongue, language
and construction clashing swords.
'Oh, what two days are on me now!'

I find there is no clear-cut Gaelic word for 'yes'.

Tonight I'm herded up these corkscrew heights –
'Na h-ainmean a tha orra' – 'That's the names
that are on them' – learning from my lips
how travelling well might not involve
the fastest route towards our mark.

Shetland

Weather clutches Lerwick by the throat
and shakes it up a little. Dwellings
shrink into their bones
like souls gazing upon the Holy Ghost.
A horizontal gale is rattling alleyways and wynds,
takes sole possession.

Far out in the Atlantic a door is shut:
the wind dives deep, emits a plunging sigh…
and then it snows. Flakes so big
they glide to earth like paper planes,
drifting and clumping, spinning
perfectly outlandish shapes,
sculpting a cold heaven of the mind.

Across the Sound of Bressay house lights wink,
shrinking the vastness, signalling
the fragile human truth of heart and hearth,
speaking of how we move the earth within our softness,
leaving distance, sea and snow behind.

Postcards of Silloth

If love is possible – and the world
is impossible without it – then it is here
among the caravans, the ornamental
rose gardens, inside Alfredo's
Rapid Pizza Palace
that we must hunt it down.

Love will pronounce itself reluctantly,
slurring after six advocaat and lemonades,
wincing and twitching
as if at any moment
you might belt it one right on the mouth
for sheer presumption. As well you might.

Love's face will open, like the over-ripe peach
it surely is. And you will notice
that Love's head is bruised
and giant – moist and buzzing
like a hive of bees. Its words are indistinct
drowned out by roaring midnight juggernauts.
You lean towards it, let it lick your ear.
Then it will lisp that famous, fatuous, line –
'Now that you've caught me, you can never leave'.

Raging round the world, somehow you end up home,
to find your letter-box is blocked
with postcard views of Silloth – docks
where hulks are rendered down to dust,
bold seas in arms against the Cambrian rock,
the chalk-mark on that pavement
where Love slipped its silver blade between your ribs.

Tom Leonard

The Common Breath
A poetic tradition

The politics of space on the page is a politics of democracy, of transference from world of text as 'the' to that of reader-subject as 'this'. It is the universalisation of the author-reader experience away from the world of passing-the-parcel to those fit to open the parcels of cultural referrents of supposedly universal value (which opening of parcels has been the industry of literary-academic exegesists this past hundred years); towards the structuring of a system of common breath, integer of the universal human.

The basis of poetry is line, the basis of prose, paragraph—most of the time. Three types of basic poetry line: as unit of metre, as unit of meaning, as unit of articulation. The politics of space belongs to the last.

The preface to Williams's 1946 *Paterson: Book One* begins colon, space.

: *a local pride;*

It is in little like the opening chords of Beethoven's third symphony of 1806. Previous givens are at the outset dispensed, we are on different ground. In Williams, the punctuation of space has arrived, as he puts it in another context, naked into the world.

Pound in 1913 had had space between words and between word and period:

The apparition   of these faces   in the crowd
                   Petals   on a wet, black   bough .

This, his first version of 'In a Station of the Metro', was visual, painterly:

> Three years ago in Paris I got out of a 'metro' train at La Concorde, and
> saw suddenly a beautiful face, and then another and another, and then a
> beautiful child's face, and then another beautiful woman, and I tried all
> that day to find words for what this had meant to me, and I could not
> find any words that seemed to me worthy, or as lovely as that sudden
> emotion. And that evening, as I went home along the Rue Raynouard, I
> was still trying and I found, suddenly, the expression. I do not mean
> that I found words, but there came an equation... not in speech, but
> in little splotches of colour. It was just that − a 'pattern,' or hardly a
> pattern, if by 'pattern' you mean something with a 'repeat' in it.

> ...And so, when I came to read Kandinsky's chapter on the language
> of form and colour, I found little that was new to me. I only felt that
> someone else understood what I understood, and had written it out
> very clearly.

It was by analogy with painting Williams later remembered the advances
in poetry of the time:

> What were we seeking? No one knew consistently enough to formulate
> a 'movement'. We were restless and constrained, closely allied with the
> painters. Impressionism, dadaism, surrealism applied to both painting
> and the poem. What a battle we made of it merely getting rid of
> capitals at the beginning of every line! The immediate image, which was
> impressionistic, sure enough, fascinated us all. We had followed Pound's
> instructions, his famous 'Don'ts,' eschewing inversions of the phrase, the
> putting down of what to our senses was tautological and so, uncalled
> for, merely to fill out a standard form. Literary allusions, save in very
> attenuated form, were unknown to us. Few had the necessary reading.

> We were looked at askance by scholars and those who turned to
> scholarship for their norm. To my mind the thing that gave us most a

49

semblance of a cause was not imagism, as some thought, but the line: the poetic line and our hopes of its recovery from stodginess.

But 1922 saw the publication of *The Waste Land*. It was pass-the-parcel time again with a vengeance.

Then out of the blue *The Dial* brought out *The Waste Land* and all our hilarity ended. It wiped out our world as if an atom bomb had been dropped upon it and our brave sallies into the unknown were turned to dust.

… the great catastrophe to our letters—the appearance of TS Eliot's *The Waste Land*. There was heat in us, a core and a drive that was gathering headway upon the theme of a rediscovery of a primary impetus, the elementary principle of all art, in the local conditions. Our work staggered to a halt for a moment under the blast of Eliot's genius which gave the poem back to the academics. We did not know how to answer him.

'The Waste Land' as it finally appeared owed much to the excisions and editing of Pound. This in part was a reflection of Pound's work-in-progress of the time and succeeding decades, the *Cantos*. The difference between Pound of the *Cantos* and Eliot of 'The Waste Land' can be seen as a difference of value accredited to fundamental voice. Both works are polyphonic and polyglottal, but Eliot's implicitly sets out high register English as the natural carrier of high cultural value: low value is set side by side in terms of irony. Goonight Lou. Hurry up please it's time. One listens to the British Council's recording of Eliot reading his own poems and one hears a voice that is more primly high-register English than the voices of most Englishmen. When Pound went to London though, his voice was apparently not so affected. This is how it was described in that city:

Pound talks like no one else. His is almost a wholly original accent, the base of American mingled with a dozen assorted 'English society' and Cockney accents inserted in mockery, French, Spanish and Greek exclamations, strange cries and catcalls, the whole very oddly inflected, with dramatic pauses and diminuendos. It takes time to get used to it, especially as the lively and audacious mind of Pound packs his speech – as well as his writing – with undertones and allusions.

This can reveal as much about the Cantos as *An Annotated Index to the Cantos of Ezra Pound*. The base American. Or as Williams again once put it:

I don't speak English, but the American idiom. I don't know how to write anything else, and I refuse to learn.

It's in his letters that Pound's variants of English are most spectacularly deployed, his typography most flamboyant with varied spelling bold capitals and lower case. These are the Cantos with his jacket off, mimicking outrage, giving advice and in-jokes and hot tips rather than formal history lessons. Pound here and in the Cantos could shift into nonstandard English as (sometimes humorous) instance of the spoken language spectrum, not as counterpoised 'bad example'. Williams, in his collage of speculative prose and poems 'Spring and All' of 1922 makes a riposte to 'The Waste Land' proclaiming 'the imagination' acting on the present instant as vital opposition to the suffocating weight of a static supposedly integral cultural past.

Our orchestra
is the cat's nuts—

Banjo jazz
with a nickelplated

amplifier to
soothe

the savage beast—
Get the rhythm

That sheet stuff
's a lot a cheese.

Man
gimme the key

and lemme loose—
I make 'em crazy

with my harmonies—
Shoot it Jimmy

Nobody
Nobody else

but me—
They can't copy it

Ending without a period. Hanging in the air. Appropriate to the music, the variations of capitals and lowercase giving fluctuated rhythm and stress that elsewhere might have been lowercase throughout for tonal consistency. The vocal intimacy of an opening line might as it were literally branch into a poem essentially mimetic as sculpture:

I must tell you
this young tree
whose round and firm trunk
between the wet

pavement and the gutter
(where water
is trickling) rises
bodily

into the air with
one undulant
thrust half its height—
and then

dividing and waning
sending out
young branches on
all sides—

hung with cocoons—
it thins
till nothing is left
but two

eccentric knotted
twigs
bending forward
hornlike at the top

The downward thrust of the progressing meaning of this Williams poem presents in inverse the upward thrust of the sycamore growth. In the same year 1927, cummings makes eye and attempted articulation of word and sentence into a jumpy imitation of a difficult carclutch.

she being Brand

-new;and you
know consequently a
little stiff i was
careful of her and(having

thoroughly oiled the universal
joint tested my gas felt of
her radiator made sure her springs were O.

K.)i went right to it flooded-the-carburettor cranked her

up,slipped the
clutch(and then somehow got into reverse she
kicked what

the hell)next
minute i was back in neutral tried and

again slo-wly;bare,ly nudg.   ing(my

lev-er Right-
oh and her gears being in
A 1 shape passed
from low through
second-in-to-high like
greasedlightning)just as we turned the corner of Divinity

avenue i touched the accelerator and give

her the juice,good

    (it

was the first ride and believe i we was
happy to see how nice she acted right up to
the last minute coming back down by the Public
Gardens i slammed on

the
internalexpanding
&
externalcontracting
brakes Bothatonce and

brought allofher tremB
-ling
to a:dead.

stand-
;Still)

Zukofsky in 1930: 'The devices of emphasising cadence by arrangement of line and typography have been those which clarify and render the meaning of the spoken word specific.'

It's a further shift again into the kinesics of the actuating breath, the canvas on which the spoken word occurs. This is where Williams' prosody was by 1946, and whereon Olson was to characterise procedure in his 'Projective Verse' essay of 1950:

> It is the advantage of the typewriter that, due to its rigidity and its space precisions, it can, for a poet, indicate exactly the breath, the pauses, the suspensions even of syllables, the juxtapositions even of parts of phrases, which he intends. For the first time the poet has the stave and the bar a musician has had. For the first time he can, without the convention of rime and meter, record the listening he has done to his own speech and by that one can indicate how he would want any reader, silently or otherwise, to voice his work.
>
> It is time we picked the fruits of the experiments of Cummings, Pound, Williams, each of whom has, after his way, already used the machine as a scoring to his composing, as a script to its vocalisation. It is now only a matter of the recognition of the conventions of composition by field for us to bring into being an open verse as formal as the closed, with all its traditional advantages.
>
> If a contemporary poet leaves a space as long as the phrase before it, he means that space to be held, by the breath, an equal length of time. If he suspends a word or syllable at the end of a line (this was most Cummings' addition) he means that time to pass that it takes the eye—that hair of time suspended—to pick up the next line. If he wishes a pause so light it hardly separates the words, yet does not want a comma—which is an interruption of the meaning rather than the sounding of the line—follow him when he uses a symbol the typewriter has to hand:
>
> 'What does not change / is the will to change'
>
> Observe him when he takes advantage of the machine's multiple margins...

The quoted line is from Olson's own 'The Kingfishers' of 1949, a reply to 'The Waste Land' of a different order. By that year Williams had published the first three books of his ongoing lyric epic *Paterson*. Space before period, word space period space in Book One:

> .   . combed into straight lines
>
>   And clerks in the post-
> office ungum rare stamps from
> his packages and steal them for their
> children's albums   .
>
> -------
>
> how much chief he may be, rather the more
> because of it, to destroy him at home   .
>
> .   .   Womanlike, a vague smile,
> unattached, floating like a pigeon
> after a long flight to his cote.

Through Book Two and Book Three the isolated period had become a regular aspect of Williams's vocabulary of space, of typographic placement. There is variation in length of space between period and word.

> a world unsuspected
>   beckons to new places
> and no whiteness (lost) is so white as the memory
> of whiteness   .
>
> With evening, love wakens
>   though its shadows
>   which are alive by reason
> of the sun shining—
>   grow sleepy now and drop away
>   from desire   .

The second isolated period is nearer the preceding word than the previous; and the next isolated period which occurs has more space before it than either of the previous two:

For what we cannot accomplish, what
is denied to love,
        what we have lost in the anticipation—
                a descent follows,
endless and indestructible   .

The spaced period can function to indicate page as canvas, score for the eye like a silent beat in music that taps the presence of rhythm even in the absence of lexical referent. To an extent the precursor is the Chinese characters of Pound's Cantos, albeit the latter are bodied as ideograms of instant meaning counterpoising meaning as sequential. But yet in counter-rhythm they function as pulse. In Williams, eye and breath become conjunctive; or as one of his late poems puts it:

undying accents
repeated till
the ear and the eye lie
down together in the same bed

Eye, ear, breath enact kinesis on page-as-canvas; Olson's essay specifies the oral and articulated: it adds ear and lungs to the play-on-the-page of the eye.

It would be wrong to privilege simplistic narratives from the complex of prosodic progress and events in the first fifty years of the twentieth century. But it seems fair to say a dialogue was one of the threads taking place between the visual—the painterly-sculptural—and the auditory—the spoken/heard, in the language. Such a dialogue occurred outside a 'mainstream' that saw itself as universal narrative in which text, form and sound worked magically within natural 'commonsensical' laws, referent and referred integrally and centrally contiguous. This takes us to the basis of colonising narrative set against a polyphonic democracy of discrete components, which the multi-voiced Paterson stands for. The 'local' here as in all of Williams's philosophy, is to privilege the everywhere here-and-now of eye and subject-voice, as against a supposed pre-existing centre of focussed value existing culturally in a privileged space historically and/ or topographically in a world essentially elsewhere. Williams's puts forward the realm of the imagination, which is a universal subject-centred property.

Variation of lefthand indent can challenge and undermine invisible (as all colonising narrative is invisible) pre-established tonal value. Likewise the challenge of lowercase. In each the focus is switched to the local, in Williams's terms, or to put it another way, to the locale of the page—and the page–reader relationship. Varying the lefthand indent could also make the base lefthand margin a musical ground upon which the play of varying indent could take place in the eye-music of ear and lungs.

For Paul Blackburn in the poems composed in the twenty years before his death in 1971 music was central:

> One of the most important things about a poem is that it is basically a musical structure and like any piece of music it needs resolution. It must tie together as a musical unit however irregular it looks upon the page.

He used regular staged indent as base, with freely varying indents, space between punctuation and word:

Procession with candles around the streets of that town:
hands raised and cupped to shield the tiny flames
    a timeless gesture
        as that slow walk
           is
from church along the main street to the second store
        then turn
           left, downslope
      to the lower street sinking past
      Ca'n Font, down
      past the lower line of houses.
Street rising gently to the road, back past
café

tailor's house

      the stairs

           the stores

                dark suits and white shirts

the line of men, dark

dresses, dark shawls, veils, the line of

women's heads down   . watching their own feet moving

      slowly   .   slowly   .   A-

                  ve, a-ve'

                  Ave Ma-ri-a,

                  A-ve, a-ve,

                  Ave Ma-ri-a

His world is always before the eye of the speaker, the kinetics before the eye of the reader. He could employ post-Poundian ideograms such as simply drawn geometric rhomboids and other shapes, silent bars / pulses stripped of all semantic referent other than the musical beat. He was a master of a visual musicality and rightly if modestly acknowledged by Creeley, in his introduction to Blackburn's *Against the Silences* as 'a far more accomplished craftsman than I.'

in this case the Pieter Stuyvesant farm, well this square

          is
          filled
          with . young . trees
          which in this case on

a minus-20 morning in February, are filled

                  with sparrows
                  screaming

as tho this snow were a spring rain somehow

    Another day (same month) another
    occurrence is clearer : off the Battery

against an ice-blue sky, some gulls
so soundlessly,
the sound of their wings is all, they
                    glide above the backs of boats, stern,
                    up, crying, or surrealisticly quiet .
And.
in the body and wings of each bird . are . go —

SUMMER CLOUDS / HIGH AND

SWIFT AGAINST THE HORIZON

                                        or else the snow .

Blackburn's poetic achievement has not yet been fully given its proper due. A couple of aspects have contributed. One is the casual observing heterosexual lust expressed by the central narrator in a deal of the poems, and lust amongst the straitlaced hypersensitive is conflated with sexism. It isn't. His narrators aren't sexist, though sometimes they might seem a bit 'oversexed' – like Burns.

More to the point, Blackburn had no fingerwagging grand-scheme cultural parcels to pass on as fundement of his work, so the university departments have had lean pickings. And there's been not much either in the schoolroom for the moral-governance unpickers of metaphor and figure of speech. The wandering eye, ear and breath of Blackburn's narrator scores and adumbrates what it sees. And this is to be slighted as 'notational'.

Yet when one looks at what Olson proclaimed in his essay, it is Paul Blackburn who most clearly subsequently carried on the principles in the succeeding twenty years. The centre of the argument, appropriately coming out of America, was a democratic one: a democracy of breath, actuated by eye and ear in the private agora of a page shared between reader and writer.

References

Pound *A Retrospect* (1917); Williams *Autobiography* 1951; letter of Iris Barry about Pound's speech quoted in *Ezra Pound: The Solitary Volcano* (Tytell) 1987; Zukofsky, *American Poetry 1920–1930*; Paul Blackburn interview 'The Sullen Art', *Nomad*, 1962.

Uilleam Blacker

Blin

Most men here go to sea. So I went to sea. That's how my father found my mother. That's where I should start. Though I don't know enough to talk about it. Because he never told me much. I can only guess. He found her in Hamburg. I don't know how she got to Hamburg. She was from St Petersburg. I think it must have been hard to get there then, that was in the 1950s. Maybe not, as I say, I don't know enough. All I know is he was in the merchant navy, and he found her in Hamburg. I often wonder how they spoke to each other then. I don't think she spoke much English, and he certainly never learned Russian. But she knew German, maybe he knew some German, though he never admitted it. They must pick something up on their travels, these men, apart from venereal diseases.

I don't know if he picked up a venereal disease, but he certainly picked up a wife. She was a Russian Jew. I'm told that makes me Jewish. I always laughed when I was told that. I thought I didn't look like a Jew, I'm green-eyed and red-haired. Then I didn't know that Jews can also be red-haired and green-eyed.

I remember her, she wasn't red-haired. She was dark, and had wiry hair, my hair is also wiry, but red. She had smooth skin that was warm, and a mark under her eye, a small birthmark. She looked like she came from a different planet from the women on the island, she was tall and graceful, and she had eyes full of intelligent far-away things. She brought a case of books with her, but they lay in the loft, she never put them out on shelves, because we didn't have any shelves, not for books. Probably he wouldn't let her. I remember them though, they were dark green and red, with no pictures on the covers, only dull black writing that was hard to make out on the dark colours. At first you thought you couldn't read it because of the dark letters on the dark cover, but actually you couldn't read it because they were different letters, they were Russian. A few years after she died a relative came and took them away. He came all the way from London to see my father, and my father gave them to him. I remember that the relative, I think he was a cousin, wanted to leave them for me, but my father said he could either take them or leave them to be burned.

He didn't like having that language around in the house, didn't like her speaking to me, though she did. That's why I still understand, why I can still speak a bit. Most of the things I can say are childish things. And I can't read, because the books were always in the case. Maybe if he had let the relative leave the books I could have learned, the relative told my father I should learn, but my father said one language was enough. He said if I wanted another language I should learn to speak Gaelic like his mother. He didn't speak it anymore. It was funny, really. Why should I learn his mother's language and not my mother's?

My father was hard to understand. He also wasn't complicated. I think that once he had been a good man. He had stories to tell, plenty of them. He talked and talked. Yes, I liked to hear them. Except when he sat with his friends and drank whiskey or rum and told some stories I didn't understand and didn't like. They made me feel sick, though I'm not sure why. Not sick like seasick, but in a different way. Now I know they are just seaman's stories, the kind every seaman has by the dozen. But then I was a boy and I didn't know that, and I didn't like them. I felt it was disrespectful to my mother. I was right too, I suppose. When I think about him and his stories, the women in them and the words they used to call the women, and his orders and curses, I don't feel like talking. I feel like shutting up all my own stories and words in a case like my mother's books. I wish my memories were in some strange writing that I couldn't read, so I couldn't recall them and tell them.

Anyway that's why I could understand her, the girl in Lisbon. That's why she laughed when I spoke to her.

It's a bad play on words, but seamen smell of semen. When they've been on the ship for weeks. When they get to a port it's coming out of their pores. When they've not seen a woman for weeks. It's a funny mixture. They want two things, two things that should go together but can't, not here, not in this port, this Hamburg or Singapore, not even in this Lisbon. They want to have a woman, as quick and hard as possible, and then they want to lie in her arms and breath deeply until they fall asleep and hopefully never wake up. But that doesn't happen. Soft arms and warm breasts do not wait on the other side of that blinding moment, that is precisely where they disappear.

By the time I made my second visit to Lisbon I understood that. I understood that, not from myself, but from the empty eyes of my shipmates as they swallowed the tail of last night's whiskey with today's beer. As they tried to wash the dirt off from the inside and couldn't. My insides were filthy too, but my eyes were not empty. It was a different filth that was inside me, that most of them didn't suspect. It was much more sinful than their filth, and it was much more delicious than their filth. I also crawled through muck in those ports, but unlike their lovers mine held on to me tight, not because they were praying hard for it to be over, but because they didn't want to let go. Their hands did not hold me the way one holds a spider as one carries it across the room and throws it from the window. Their hands held me like a child grips its mother. I did not have to drag my rough words of proposition through the thick air like a rope, and hear sharp voices cut them with a number. We mostly said nothing.

Sometimes, like that night, it was impossible to get away. Our group did not drink itself into dispersion before the brothel, so I ended up in a room with her. I could see right away she was from the same regions as my mother. Not because she looked like my mother. This girl was Slavic. There were always girls with those cheekbones, those oval eyes, that hard stare in every port. I would hear them murmur sometimes in the half-forgotten words of that language I never really knew, or in some language that shared with it those words that prostitutes might murmur.

It wasn't the first time. So what do you do? You pay, you wait, you smoke a cigarette and you leave, then you make up a story, if you have to. Mostly we didn't ask each other.

I went in to the room after her. A paper sheet, like from a hospital, was laid on the bed, and it made a crumpling sound as she sat down on it. She began to get undressed. I went to the window, opened it and began to smoke with my back to her. I breathed out into the black, night-time street. The silence was broken by a snapping sound, some button or catch breaking, and she cursed under her breath. She cursed softly, using a delicate word instead of a coarse one. *Ay, blin!* she said.

Ay, blin! was what my mother used to say, because a coarse word would never enter her head, far less leave her mouth. It shares its first two letters with the coarsest and most common interjection in Russian, a word that means whore. *Blin* replaces it on delicate and intelligent lips. It always stayed with her, that small word. In those split seconds when her guard was down, when she dropped something or looked out of the window and saw it was raining on the washing, it could see its chance and came rushing back to her lips, like a mischievous cat escaping through a closing door.

I looked out at the street, an empty back street. I pulled back the focus of my eyes and looked at my reflection in the glass. I looked at the empty alleyway running through my dark reflection. I saw her light reflection, sitting on the reflection of the bed, under the reflection of the harsh, pale light of a bare bulb. I saw the dark reflection of her underwear.

'Hey', I heard her say quietly. 'Time!' Of course, I didn't have all night.

I smiled at her reflection and breathed a long plume of smoke out of the open half of the window, across the empty alleyway. I turned and looked at the scene before me, cursing my luck with a smile, cursing the pale light that fell on the skin of her thin arms, cursing this room I was in, far away from a dark and cosy corner, no strong arm around my waist.

'*Mozhet, nie nado…*' I smiled at her. I felt I must have looked tired in that moment. She laughed, but without smiling.

'*Sho, pederas?*' she asked coldly, not in the least relieved or amused.

I was incapable of anything more witty than 'Da' in reply. I smiled, sure she should see the funny side eventually. She looked at me. Her face showed no reaction. Only her body seemed to relax, to sink a little, to become softer.

'*Nu, shto podelayesh? Zaplatish?*' she asked.

'*Kanyeshno,*' I assured her.

'*Nu, blin!*' she breathed, and flopped back on the paper sheet. It must have been unpleasant to lie on, I thought. She lay there, pale and black on the white sheet, and grew soft, seemed to blur. It was as though I couldn't quite see her, as though I were imagining or remembering her not quite clearly.

I had always thought it funny that my mother said 'pancake' when something bad happened. *Blin.* I remember laughing when she told me what it meant. I remember thinking how funny it would be to say *blin* on dropping a pancake on the floor, or getting it stuck to the ceiling. I never did. I don't remember her making pancakes.

It was strange it had never crossed my mind before. How often I'd wondered how my father, a dour Scottish sailor, had ended up with my mother, a Russian emigrant, in a German port in the 1950s. What circumstances could have brought them together, and what could have made her want to go with him to the other end of Europe, where her books would be locked up, where she would stand out among the other women, and where her son would laugh at the strangeness of the simplest of words?

I turned away again as the girl dressed herself. A silent *blin* slipped across my lips with the last smoke of my cigarette.

Note

Mozhet, nie nado: Maybe we don't have to
Sho, pederas?: What, you a fag?
Nu, shto podelayesh? Zaplatish?: What can you do? You going to pay?
Kanyeshno: Of course

Fred Johnston

Ship of Fools

> *He last on this savage promontory shored*
> *His logical weapon…*
>
> Richard Murphy: *Wittgenstein and the Birds*

The boat groaned in on an unusually high tide.

Rusting in the masts and sides, some sort of name painted over on the stern, it appeared lashed to our stone quay like an old sea story. From the start, no one wanted it there, it stank almost visibly.

He put it about that he was a refugee from something hideous in darker middle Europe. There was a romantic touch of the gypsy on him. He said he had been a painter. Often in the following days he was to be seen painting something, God knows where he came by the materials. He would sit by the quayside and paint their hideous boat. When the tide went out the vessel leaned precariously against the quay wall, a tired old rogue of a thing, a hulking embarrassment.

The rest of them appeared in and out the local pubs, following fiddlers and singers and tapping the sides of their beer glasses with combs and other objects, putting on some show of being primal and in contact with the music of the earth, I suppose. I've been working in the Life Assist Centre for long enough and I've seen this sort of thing before. They come in, dubious Cockneys, they look for advice on how to mend their lives, not really wanting it, I suspect. I point them in the direction of the dole. Everyone's happy.

The Life Assist Centre is a neglected place, dragged down by the weight of hopelessness shoved into its insatiable mouth every open day. I dress casual, you're supposed to. Nothing officey, nothing intimidating. But it's myself who feels intimidated. On the walls there are displayed all the hopeless under-classy posters of a new world if you'll only sign this, ask about that. In truth there is no saving a whole swathe of people. There are things you cannot say openly and that's one of them.

So when he came in, smiling that appalling, uncomprehending smile, I smiled back as I'm supposed to and prepared myself for the usual helpful rituals. He was young enough under the earthy untidiness. He wore the sort of brown tweedy jacket that much older men, farmers, perhaps, wear to tend cattle and do other messy jobs. His white shirt collar was filthy, his hair short, black and greasy. You look at people like that and say, 'There but for the Grace…' It's hard not to despise them.

'I can teach to paint.'

'Your name is?'

'Painting. I can do.'

He made birdy shapes in the air, or so I interpreted the fine, almost delicate wavings of his long pianist's paint-stained fingers. They'd been around for a week, near enough, with their dreadful boat. What, I wondered, were the three or four others, a long-skirted, barefoot girl among them, doing while he was mouthing in front of me.

'I must have your name.'

I'd produced a form to hide behind. Over his shoulder in the sloping empty street a sunlight of sorts quivered and slopped against the grey pavements. The village had a writers' group and amateurish workshops on print-making, pottery, even Tarot-card reading. Blow-ins like myself, some of them retired from the world, others just young and strangely sad, ran most of them. Perhaps he'd be lucky.

His name was unpronounceable, of course. He spelt it for me, coming close, his breath unhealthy and hot and thick on my face. His clothes smelled of cigarettes and stale beer and sweat. I wrote it down. Was it like this for bored officials at Ellis Island? This making and remaking of language? Conjuring up identities?

I scribbled, guessing him into comprehensible existence. I showed him what I'd written. He frowned, then perhaps thought not to unbalance things. He nodded vigorously. We went through a similar ritual over his age. Place of birth?

His story bore the strained rhythm of a recitation, a poem at a reading, intonations here and there for effect; a story whose truth was hidden under too many applied coats of panic and loss. The more he acted, the more I knew he was describing truth as a kaleidoscope of probabilities. It was an odd moment or two. Perhaps he had learned that the truth without gestures only weighs half as much. Or perhaps it was the weak sun brightening the street over his shoulder and the mood I was in.

I mentioned his painting. Animated again, this time all movement funnelled through his round brown eyes, he spoke of a city the vowels of whose name I barely caught, a university. There was tragedy of a sort in the story, foreign and alien tragedy, all the more romantic and unreal for its cargo of distance and exotic place-names. In any case, he'd met his odd friends the boat people and landed here, a bare village by the wide ocean with a broken castle and new bungalows painted pink for the new young rich from elsewhere; foreigners, so far as the locals were concerned, like himself.

But he wasn't one of them, no. He tried to make that clear. He was a good man, he said.

Mischievously, I held my tongue, resisted the urge to tell him it didn't matter, that he'd never be anything but an outsider here. Let him learn for himself. I'd even seduced some local women to gain acceptance, but it hadn't worked, I broke no silence when I entered a pub. And they were the sorts of women who giggled in the pubs afterwards and had known one another since schooldays. They were going nowhere, there was no need for them ever to grow up. Schoolgirls they'd be still, at sixty. Through them, I frustrated myself the more.

A brief slither of resentment caressed my abdomen like an unwanted hand. My life was a small round thing, rolled up and down that sloping street behind this immigrant's back. He showed me papers, complex things with green harps on them. I ignored them. Suddenly I was tired and irritated.

'Write a notice,' I told him, my voice raised for no reason. I pointed to the wall, to the mean window: 'I'll put it up for you on the wall. There. An advertisement. Don't forget to hand it to me.'

I spoke slowly, as you would to a child.

Of course, he must hand it to me. I would be the one to physically tack it to the wall, tape it on the window; you had to make some show of authority. Couldn't have him thinking he had a right to do it himself.

'Yes,' he nodded, obviously relieved. 'Thank you, yes.'

He backed out of the front door. Over his head, dangling from the wall, flapped a flightless poster of a pregnant teenager and the words Scared? Lonely?

Evening threw marvellous sky-colours over the prim, settled harbour. Small rowing boats jiggled here and there, from bigger yachts there came the fairy belling of metal clamps, rings, a thousand other bits and pieces, and a triangle of swans cleaved the blue dark water off the stony, wrack-black shore. There were clouds over the far islands, brewing up out of the western ocean. A breeze ran before them. The odour of salt, brine, ammonia hung in the air like smoke; a dog scampered on a thin stretch of trimmed grass, pissing from ancient stone bollard to bollard. The great dead stone warehouse, windows shut like the eyes of the dead, faced the bracing new sea wind and the coming smack of rain, stared eyeless over the rolling masts and the ropes and the furring sea and the rusty, ugly bulk of the vessel upon which my client had arrived.

This, then, was my nightly walk home. I took it all in, its utter, even sunny loneliness, its village terror like a child's fear of the dark muttering under everything. Scraps of old rumour hung from the trees, crows gossiped on the rooftops. Or round the ceiling of my skull, at least.

Sadness came with the drop of the working day. In the pitiful office I had at least a sense of purpose and of myself. Alone, walking where eager tourists took photographs and pointed camcorders and said aloud how lovely everything was, I felt a cold sadness like a small death flowering in me. I went in to The Gravel Walks.

There was a photograph on a mock-stone wall of what the pub had been like twenty years ago, a small thatched place with black-capped, crow-like men outside it. A whole field had been swallowed up by the new place, a green-painted two-storey building with mock-wooden pillars and plastic lifebelts, lobsters and even plastic nets, prefabricated, a sort of big child's kit, splattered everywhere inside. A fake ancient map showed where a slice of island had been born out of the Great Portuguese Earthquake. The music from the bat-like speakers on the walls was bumpa-bumpa-bumpa trash of the sort kids do drugs to and die by.

Over the mirror behind the glistening, whitewood bar hung proudly a photograph of the proprietor with his arm around the shoulders of a recently disgraced politician. There was a piano in one corner of the room and the room was mushroomed with small round tables and stools. The TV was always on, even with the music from the speakers, even when a few local musicians played their jigs and reels in the corner at weekends.

A couple of elderly locals in caps turned to look at me as I came in. There was no hint of friendliness. The white-shirted barman kept his head down and polished glasses fussily, talking into the floor. Every now and then one of his customers would nod. I grabbed a rattled copy of the Daily Mirror, glanced at pregnant superstars and read a couple of paragraphs on two schoolboys accused of decapitating a neighbour's cat. Over whiskey and water and a toasted cheese sandwich, its cellophane wrapping melted into the bread, I stared over the long barren field of evening.

Towards closing-time a healthy argument about music, politics and Gaelic football, about which I knew nothing, had eased a gathering isolation.

It was, I suspected, an isolation felt by all of us, the stalwart half-dozen, who perched and swivelled on our bar stools like exotic yapping birds. Someone mentioned the hulking boat in the harbour, the filth of it and of its long-haired crew. And that foreigner, that Pole, or Russian, or whatever he was. Jesus! The village was a refugee camp!

I despised these bitter, destroyed half-farmers, half-fishermen, glistening with the beery sweat of their various lonely dooms. Yet I nodded as if something controlled me, something outside myself pulled the strings. I went home with back-slappings and the smack of chilled, white salted air in the face. I abhor injustice. I made coffee, put some paper in the ancient Oliver typewriter, wrote a letter to a local newspaper. It doesn't matter what I wrote about. The pressure of my fingers on the old keys was reassuring at first, then exciting. There was power here in what I was doing. I was reaching out into the world. A sadness, heavy and dark, filled me when I'd finished. I read over my letter. I found an envelope, a stamp, posted the letter at the end of a long, silent walk along the quays to the Post Office slot in the wall.

Then I walked back again, meeting no one, drenched in the salty darkness, ears full of the sing-song tinkle of the rocking boats.

I saw him once or twice over the coming weeks, the painter. He smiled broadly at me, as if he were a schoolboy under surveillance. Look how well I'm doing. The sadness in all of this was too much for me to look at. I hated seeing him, dreaded that he would ever come over to me, say anything. By this time he had acquired a couple of teenage students and they huddled in front of the harbour on good weather days with their sketch pads and even their rudimentary watercolour sets or important-looking tins of paint, children enjoying themselves, feeling themselves to be different.

The others from the boat haunted the pubs where listless, half-hearted jigs and reels were played, and they joined in the dreary ballads of young men dying for Ireland's freedom, miming the words. By this, I suppose, they imagined it was possible to blend in to the village, or some aspect of it. I knew better. Acceptance here was not a song you could sing or imitate. No outsider knew the music of this village.

When the weather blew up, the painter would adjourn his classes. His pupils, clutching round him for a brief moment out of courtesy, would then disperse. When he was accused, under the breath, of inviting the teenagers on to the rusting vessel, I knew it was a lie. So did the bar-stool retailer of the libel. But it didn't matter.

Arguments, raised voices, were now common in the smokey, brown-aired music pubs. One of the painter's boat companions would attempt a song, something daftly Irish such as 'Carrickfergus'. At once an ancient huddle at the bar would turn drunkenly, mutter unintelligibly but loudly. Interrupted, the singer would ask for quiet; worse, he would ask, in that mock-Cockney which by now irritated us all, for respect. I would stand by a door, glass in hand, my mouth leprous with nicotine, and take a brazen delight in the young man's helplessness. Someone had remarked that they'd seen a letter of mine in the paper; he could not recall its subject. But this conferred upon me a certain status. So I smiled with the rest as the hated youth, his song dead, twisted a rat's tail of hair in his dirty-nailed fingers and stared around the room. Some local girls, too young to be served in a public bar but getting drunk there anyway, eyed up the strangers. Further proof, of course, of their inherent evil. In shops, fat middle-aged women, all trace of femininity erased, worn down, would speak in harsh men's voices about castrating anyone who made a daughter of theirs pregnant.

I'd been long enough in the village to know this would happen anyway; I had my brace of single mothers, children themselves, red-eyed, harassed, struggling to maneouvre the push-chairs over the single step, troop into the Life Assist Centre before the hell-ship had docked.

I could feel the air thicken over the village, giving us something new and thrilling to breathe. Not the salt of the sea now but the salt of blood, an envigorating, lusty tang, almost sexual. The weather changed and stayed, hot and starry in its daily turn. In the Centre I stripped down to my shirt and rolled up the sleeves. I felt rakish and younger. The painter came in, wide-faced with fear and agitation.

'My paints, brushes,' he stuttered. His hands flew like scared birds. 'What about them?'

It was a beautiful day. He was a speck in the day's clear eye.

'They have been robbed of me! I have nothing.'

I felt the weight of his nothing. It was a particular thing, it had a certain unforgettable taste, I'd sipped it once or twice. I did not want intimations of this nothingness pleading with me to be recognised. His brown, gypsy face fascinated me in its agitation. His flying ringless hands were now the brown leaves of a tree dancing at the end of the thin branches of his arms. He was a tree, black against the sun of the sloped street outside, interfering with the passage of the good white light.

'Talk to the police, then.'

They would take no notice, of course. But he knew this from God only knew what number of previous lives.

He shook his head, assumed a solemn expression. Absurdly I recalled the barman's ignorant habit of addressing you while staring at the floor. The world was full of simple ignorance.

'I don't understand how you think I can help you, then. This is the wrong place.'

The last phrase slipped out and I heard it even before I spoke it. Yes, this was indeed the wrong place, for both of us. Something mischievous or even malign had thrown us into this village, searching for better things, a life, love, whatever. We'd run aground on the arid shores of village life. The village spoke about me behind my back as surely as they spoke of him behind his.

But I resented him the more for knowing this. No one had the right to consider him my equal in any sense. No one had the right to judge us on the same terms. He was a fucking foreigner, for God's sake. Christ, he looked like a tinker!

My outrage, his dwindling complaint, met in the stale hot cigarettey air of the single room of the Centre.

And I noticed his smell. Or perhaps it was my own.

I opened my arms and hands in a pontiff-like gesture.

'I'm afraid we can't supply money for things like paint and brushes, if that's what you want.'

This was not strictly true. But I had no intention of going through elaborate procedures with him or indicating other services which might help him. I felt the power, the drunkenness, of having him at my mercy. Behind him, a shadow flew down the sloping street, then the sun whitewashed everything. I had an image of how nice it would be to tramp up over the mountains on a day like this, the breeze blushing your face, the sea below you all the way to America.

The door behind him opened and an old man came in. The painter turned, saw the old man, gave a slight bow and left without another word.

Not long after that the graffiti appeared. Scrawled along the side of the boat nudging the quay, the grand, righteous word *pervarts*. With an 'a'. It went with the utterly unfounded rumour that the painter was taking local children on board the boat. You heard this sort of thing in the Gents in The Gravel Walks. The stink of urine carried the words into your nostrils, burned them there.

Tourists arrived, buses bigger than the world, purring outside our ruins while dangerously fat people in whites and yellows and oranges and blues and even stripes drank Guinness and photographed each other drinking Guinness. They crawled over our ancient castle like gaudy ants. The sun glossed the small waves of the harbour, the water turned a Pacific blue. The sunsets were read and clear-skied. Schoolgirls smoked illicit cigarettes under the awning of the rusting, piss-smelling bus shelter and eyed the French teenagers, the small Japanese adolescents with their forever smiles and e-cameras, the Yank guys, gawky and dangerously innocent, with their peaked caps on backwards.

The world came to the village, polishing it up. Musicians came from all over the county to play in the pubs, too-fast jigs and reels, hopelessly bad

Country 'n' Irish. Tourists tried to sing Irish songs under the pale eye of hand-held video cameras. There was money going round, there were rivers of piss in the early morning streets, yellowish vomit hardening in the morning sunlight on the pavements. Empty cigarette-packets and used condoms married in the gutters. The sound of glass breaking mixed with loud laughter and the hysterical, whining woman's screel of bows across fiddle-strings. The midday Mass every Sunday was in Irish, which the Catholic American tourists loved. It reminded him of the days of Latin, one of them told me; what you can't understand stays magical.

The painter had obtained, as if by a dark magic of his own, more paints, brushes, and he sat sketching and painting down by the quayside every morning and for an hour or two after lunch, eating soup and bread rolls and drinking black coffee in The Gravel Walks. No one made any remarks about him. It wouldn't have done to have upset the munching and drinking tourists sitting around and about. Some perverse and mercenary reasoning had set him up there, unwitting, as a living advertisement for the cultural diversity of the village. Look at us, the village seemed to say through him; look how colourful and rich is our understanding of the world.

His companions from the boat gathered around him on the quayside, sipping from tins of cider or smoking joints. The rich aroma of hashish drifted over the stones and the sea and the tourists turned up their noises and frowned. But he sold a painting here and there. The others, I'd no doubt, lived off him. He smiled a lot. Perhaps in some men that's a sign of their knowledge of impending disaster. The music rattled and screeched like bad brakes out of every pub door, the vomiting in the street continued, the grunting and drunken heaving and bucking against the old brick walls gasped on.

In the wee hours of one of these amazed mornings, fire broke out on the boat. The painter and two others, asleep, were trapped and suffocated. The fire licked upwards through the messy rigging; I can imagine stars of fire burning into the wide open black heavens. It was muttered that the painter's body had been found with the hands outstretched, claws of hands. Men and women hungry for horror said things like this. There was also an element of the exotic and thrilling in the notion of fire twisting the stranger's body into something unimaginably un-human. Certainly I hoped that he hadn't woken up, that his paints and thinners had burned him quickly. I had obsessional spurts of grotesque images, his mouth crisped back off his teeth, his tongue black, swollen, that idiot smile of his etched into his skull with fire. Perhaps I had the ugliness in my head already and I needed it to have a face, something vaguely human.

The fat red growling fire engines on the quay brought out the tourists' cameras. Then there were the police, striding big men in civvies who drove flash cars with city polish on their dark sleek metal; men who ignored the local Guards, who had, it seemed, nothing in common with them. The ambulances took the bodies away, covered stretchers moving in grey speed from the cordoned-off blackened boat to the white immaculateness of the bright lights of their silver and white interiors. Such a miracle of movement on the village quay that day.

The deaths quietened us for a time. A Mass was said to a packed church. Flowers came out of nowhere, crinkling cellophaned bunches laid on the altar rails. Meanwhile, the bodies were in a mortuary somewhere. The Mass, I sensed, was not so much about the strange dead but about ourselves, we who had been there before them; it was an exorcism of sorts. If there was guilt, the Mass removed it; we smoked outside on the steps, annoyed that the service had taken so long, the weather fine and cool, the trees fat with black birds and their high nests, every wrinkle in the plump distant mountains visible and distinct. There was an unspoken agreement, like a virus carried in the air, that no one had an opinion to share about the cause of the fire.

Days follow days and he stays with me. My roomy clutter contains one of his paintings, gaudy unnatural colours but bright, bright. No one knows I purchased one from him, a view of our ruined castle with the sea splashed in black blue all around it. Nothing moves in the picture, neither human being nor flying bird. Even the water is frozen.

I remember him, I see him painting on the quay and I see him pleading in front of me at the Centre. How little I know of him beyond these images. He is a cypher, a ghost, moving in and out of himself, in and out of the mind of the village I have made, or tried to make, my own. So it is that it is possible that the sloping main street and the old grey stones and salt-rotted red brick of disused buildings contain him, or that part of him which rises upwards and becomes local memory.

National newspapers have sent their perfumed columnists and small town Irish life has been called many things. Suddenly the village is older, blacker, more dangerous. The Famine graveyard on the top of the hill is haunted by journalists trying to get background, a feel for place.

The police investigation is still going on, they're never far away, obvious in their ordinary clothes, sipping drinks, watching, listening. They are civil and will strike up a conversation with you as good as any one. But they are listening with their voices, you can see that.

Men whose lives are dead leaves on a pond, dried up inside from lack of women or mother loss or God knows what, mutter drunkenly about how no good could possibly follow people like that, the outsiders.

The word outsider has taken on a different resonance, significance, than foreigner. Language is shifting, sprouting new fruit, day to day as the deaths by fire on the boat become more real.

I do not know what to think about the fire that killed him. I remember him and his smile and how I enjoyed him being lower in the village social scale than myself and that is all. I enjoy my guilt, live off it. I've been drawn closer to the village by my having been here when he died. There was something, I suppose, absurdly sacred about what happened to him. Those others of his companions drifted away, the not unattractive girl with them; the boat hulks still, rust the colour of blood, blackening, no gulls will settle on any part of her.

As our language alters in the very air around me, as people greet me every day in the street and stop and discuss the weather, cows calving, someone building a currach, his face takes on an ikonic glow in my memory. Now they call me *the writer* because of all those letters of mine that appear in newspapers.

But I do not know who to defend next. A new world slinks forward, drooling. Lawyers send warning letters to newspapers. Writers sue one another. The world is heavier than it has ever been. The poets are dead or dying. Nothing is true. We are warned, we are warned; the rooms in which we try to breathe begin to shrink.

Yet we must be involved.

Robin Gillanders—Highland Journey

Using a large format camera and black and white film, photographer and author Robin Gillanders chronicled a three-month journey around the Highlands in an old campervan. With the shower converted into a darkroom, film processing could take place 'on the road', following a tradition of itinerant photographers pioneered by Roger Fenton during the Crimean War. (Images and text from *Highland Journey: In the Spirit of Edwin Muir* are reproduced with the kind permisssion of Birlinn.)

Pass of Drumochter

This is the gateway to the Highlands, travelling from Edinburgh to Inverness, and carries the essentials of modern communication. Edwin Muir referred to this as the Great North Road. Now, less romantically, it's just the A9. The Pass is the highest point on any railway in Britain.

Pearl McKenna & 'Nipper', The Royal Oak, Dufftown

There is a real feeling that this is a working town with a purpose – principally Walker's Shortbread and whisky. This also brings tourism, but with two chip shops and two wee supermarkets this is surely an index of an indigenous population and not just passing or hotel-staying tourists.

The Royal Oak is a traditional Scottish pub – no frills. Pearl is originally from Glasgow and hers is an easy and relaxed friendliness – not put on, showy, or disingenuous. Like the bar itself.

John Richard, Cooper, Speyside Cooperage

Having just finished his four-year apprenticeship, he is engaged to be married to Pearl's barmaid and has no plans to leave, as many young people do. Whisky is one of the major export industries of the Highlands and a principal employer in Speyside. This is the only independent family-run cooperage left in the Highlands.

Fishing Net Drying Poles, Portmahomack

Herring and whitefish were a major employer on the East Coast throughout the nineteenth century, reaching its peak before World War One, after
which it went into steady decline. This was for a variety of reasons, but
included a decrease in the markets of Germany and Russia and later because
of over-fishing. Now there is some in-shore fishing for prawns (sold as lang-
oustines!) and lobsters, but mainly fishing is for leisure, and since the oil
platform construction yard opened at nearby Nigg in 1972, most fishermen
left their nets to work there.

A century ago the population would double during the season with hundreds of boats and attendant herring curers coming in. Now it probably
doubles in the summer with tourists, holiday-homers – and campers.

Liz White, The Railway Hotel, Tain

Tain seems a genteel and attractive town and yet karaoke and discos have arrived. The town has attempted to deal with youth problems – mainly involving alcohol. Liz's bar runs a disco on a Friday and Saturday and has three bouncers on the door.

Liz came to Tain twenty-four years ago with her husband, who worked at Nigg. A lot of Glaswegians came up to work there – houses were built for them in Alness and when the work dried up many of them stayed. Liz's husband left and she stayed on and now manages the hotel. She has the same easy, undemonstrative friendliness that Pearl in Dufftown has.

Dominic Cooper, Writer & Poet, Ardnamurchan

Many artists and writers have come to the Highlands to seek a more solitary and stress-free existence. Some only come for the summer months, but Dominic has lived here permanently for many years and derives considerable inspiration from Celtic culture and the land.

Electricity Supply, Ardnamurchan

The spread of electricity to even the most remote communities, followed by the telephone, television and the internet, has greatly facilitated communications over the last couple of decades. This has meant that a greater range of employment opportunities have opened up, including working from home; but it has also signalled a decline in close-knit communities and an increase in global influences.

Cragaig, Mull

This tiny village was abandoned, not due to the 'clearances', as so many were, but voluntarily when the plague arrived from Ireland. Dominic Cooper, who based his acclaimed book *The Dead of Winter* on Cragaig, wrote:

Maybe Cragaig itself is not important except as a representation of all the emptied Highlands. That beautifully built wall and corner which, at the time, was a skill of such necessity. Its beauty of line much more than beauty for beauty's sake: a beauty that was man's vital attempt to dovetail himself into the harsher beauties of nature – for the corner of the building is both tapered and rounded so as to take the wind. The abandonment of these 'remote' world centres may be seen as the beginning of the abandonment of community, and of the self as part of community; as the beginning of the modern individual's obsession with self and all material things. I have always felt that the loss of this community bonding, as well as the loss of our earthing in the soil, was the beginning of the disintegration of all natural happiness. And was the beginning of the necessity for psychiatrists.

K.C. Mackinnon, Sheepdog Trials, Strathcarron

Shepherds come from all over the Highlands to these trials, which take place in several locations over the summer months. This is KC Mackinnon with his dogs, Bob and Corrie, over from Skye. I don't think anybody knows what his first name actually is…

Sheepdog trials are a valuable component of Highland community life – and they are popular with tourists despite the fact that it always seems to rain…

Musicians, Applecross Inn

A sense of community and Highland cultural identity in part resides in music and the 'social arts'. Not just the tours by well-known performers, but in local talent. Sean was born in Applecross but moved away for many years, to return only recently; Helena is from Bristol and works in the Inn.

Immigrant Workers, Ullapool

Ola Witkowska, Receptionist, Poland; Stefan Laktis, Chef, Slovakia; and Cyril Mkhize, Kitchen porter, South Africa

The hotel trade in the Highlands has long relied on immigrant seasonal workers. Jean Urquhart, the owner of The Ceilidh Place in Ullapool, feels privileged to have people from different cultures working for her. In the 1970s it was Filipinos; in the '80s and '90s it was mainly Australians working to finance a holiday; now it's Eastern Europeans who come for economic reasons. Jean feels it would be awful if Scotland were only populated with Scots.

Fish Farm Workers, Scourie

James Forsyth (senior skipper) and Duncan Morrison (crewman)

Fish farming is one of the fastest growing sectors of the world food economy, especially in the Highlands. This one near Scourie is one of the most environmentally sustainable in the Highlands – but the whole issue of aquaculture causes strong debate over its impact on Scotland's fragile marine environment.

Passing Place, Forsinard, Caithness (cover image)

The Flow Country is an immense peatland, the largest expanse of blanket bog in Europe sustaining a diversity of wild life under the protection of the Forsinard Nature Reserve. Besides bird-watching, paradoxically, hunting, fishing and shooting are important elements of tourism here.

Regi Claire

Russian Blue

The day I got away from the White Coats behind the mountains I laughed for the first time in months. A laugh that seemed to stall and stutter until my whole being was bursting with it and there was no space left for the memory of Cupid-bow smiles and casual arm-locks, the chemical cocktails and bland food, no space left any more for that puke-pastel building flanked by cypresses like guards on permanent duty.

By then, of course, I had long crossed the river flowing past it all so demurely, in its straitjacket of concrete, and was well on my way.

They'd said I needed help, lots of help. Bribe a doctor, two doctors, some specialist and, hey bingo, she's all yours! But I was never theirs, whatever they might have thought. And they didn't help me either – I helped myself. Did what they wanted until I was allowed art therapy (with access to scissors, paints, fabrics, adhesives) to 'express myself'. That same night, I hacked my hair down to a stubble, wrapped a bandage round my chest and dressed in a set of men's clothes from the recycling bin. A dab of paint, some glue and jute, and I became Bernhard Neumann, slightly down-at-heel, swarthy, moustachioed, with a voice that seemed to growl and the sad brown eyes of a St Bernard.

They must have reported me missing the moment my room was found empty next morning. Posters, dusty by now and bleached by the summer heat, would have been tacked to the walls of police and railway stations, libraries, doss-houses, to telegraph poles and the trunks of the weeping willows in my hometown. Below the picture of a frumpy, middle-aged woman called Clara Kummer, a 'greatly worried' husband would have been mentioned, though not the fact that he never once bothered to visit her in all the time the White Coats kept her locked up.

With barely two hundred francs saved from my 'personal luxuries' allowance, I made it to the Alps by the end of August, walking, hitching, picking fruit or vegetables in return for a hot meal and a bed, even begging on occasion. A generous farmer on Lake Constance had let me have his old pup tent and rucksack (with a Swiss Army Knife inside), and I'd got hold of a baseball cap and a pair of horn-rimmed glasses at a flea market. No one would have recognised in Bernhard Neumann the good little wife-cum-cookery-teacher who'd always given outdoor activities a wide berth.

It was after a misty-golden trek along the lakes of the Upper Engadine and down the vertiginous drop of Maloja Pass into Val Bregaglia that I came across the Russian Blue.

Near the Italian border I'd climbed a steep mountain track past terraces of chestnut trees and tiny orchards of wasp-riddled fruit, unpruned vines and benches furred with moss and orange lichen towards a small settlement of houses. Even from a distance I could see the gaping holes in the roofs, black spaces in the mosaic of grey, ochre and silver-green granite tiles where birds flew in and out freely. The wooden verandas and balconies sagged as if under the combined weight of generations. The houses had been abandoned years ago.

Looking for a place to spend the night, I had just squeezed through a cellar door stuck permanently half-open when there was a miaow from the shadowy depths. Seconds later I felt something rub against my legs. The cat was beautiful, almost luminous in the semi-darkness, thin yet elegant like one of those Egyptian goddesses – and a bit like a ghost, too, with its bluish quicksilver coat, eerily prominent whisker pads and vivid green eyes: a ghost cat in a ghost house in a village full of ghost houses.

I backed away and the creature disappeared without a sound; for a moment I wondered if I'd merely imagined it, giving physical existence to a passing thought. I blame the White Coats for these flashes of unease, messing me up with their drugs.

But then, pushing my way out into the wind that had begun to smell of rain, I heard the miaow again, sharp this time and much louder, terminating in a heart-rending whimper – almost human-sounding. Despite my fear and an inner voice urging me to get the hell out, I couldn't resist following what was by now no more than an echo in my ears. I kept slipping on the damp cellar cobbles, stepped on debris that scrunched unnervingly under my feet, stepped into soft, wet, squishy things I preferred to think were old newspapers soaked to a pulp by decades of neglect. Then I reached another door, solid and slightly ajar. I inched it open with my walking stick.

No grisly secrets; the room was filled with firewood in straggly piles. Yet, for an instant, the scaly, discoloured branches reminded me of snakes poised to strike and I felt my insides go liquid with fear. The light had a sluggish, muddy quality, as if tainted by the only window, narrow, high up and thick with grime and cobwebs.

A sudden movement to my left made me recoil. The cat had emerged from round a heap of logs stacked into a low wall, its silver-blue coat near-electric. Its tail was up and the large ears seemed even more pointed as it stared at me, solemn and unblinking. After a while it arched its graceful neck and started rubbing against my legs, purring. I bent down to stroke it. Just then, there was a noise behind the logs.

I raised my stick. 'Who's there?' My voice was a squeak of tangled vocal cords.

No one answered. The cat had darted away again, and all I could hear were the usual creakings, drippings and barely audible moanings, the bodily functions of most derelict buildings – before a volley of raindrops hit the windowpane like shrapnel.

I gripped my stick harder. 'Come on! Show yourself!'

Still no reply.

The cat gave another of its peremptory miaows and returned. It stopped a little in front of me, then took a couple of steps towards the stack of logs… stopped and looked back at me… took a few more steps… stopped… looked. Finally I followed.

The first thing I noticed were the brightly coloured women's clothes scattered around a large sports bag: a gentian-blue cardigan, a green silk blouse, a purple dress and matching underwear. An earthenware jug stood in a wet patch by the wall, next to a single purple stiletto and a carrier bag spilling chocolate wrappers, empty tins and crisp packets. I was about to crouch down for a better look when the cat miaowed again. It was sitting motionless behind another, smaller stack of logs and gazing at me. I smiled: of course, it wanted to show me its litter!

I approached cautiously – approached a wadded-up blanket on top of a sheet of plastic and some newspapers...

No, it was impossible! I turned away. How cruel the human mind can be, clawing at the very centre of one's heart, tearing it apart. I took several slow, deep breaths, then glanced over once more. But the baby was still there, tucked inside the blanket.

I dropped to my knees, put down my walking stick. The baby's eyes were closed. Saliva had dried on its chin. The lips were slack and waxy pale. As I looked into the tiny face, it seemed to dissolve into a translucency of skin, hair and bone. My fingers left silvery trails on the baby's cheeks. So cold, they felt, as cold and implacable as the mountains standing guard behind the house.

All of a sudden the little mouth quivered. I snatched my hand away. The cat flicked the tip of its tail, stared at me with blade-thin pupils and lay down beside the baby, one front paw curled protectively across the blanket. As it did so, a flat round piece of wood the size of a pocket mirror slid from the fabric folds.

I picked it up. The icon was amateurish, kitschy even, but it cut me to the quick all the same. I felt as if I had violated a shrine, broken a spell or some kind of promise. How could I have forgotten about the baby's mother? She'd be nearby, had perhaps gone foraging for berries and sweet chestnuts and was now sheltering from the rain I could hear pelting down. But she wouldn't leave her child alone for long. No mother would. Though a few minutes could do it – ten minutes was enough, after all, one short trip to the baker's up the street for a loaf of bread – and the guilt would last a lifetime. In spite of what the White Coats said. They didn't understand, could never understand, not with all the training, textbooks and therapy in the world.

My scars had started to itch. I got to my feet, pulled back the sleeves of my leather jacket and those of my woollen jumper, then drew my wrists up and down the dirty wall, roughly, again and again, gritting my teeth until the pain made me gasp. Afterwards I hugged the wounds to myself like precious gifts. Bloodletting always helped to soothe me – and it still does, sometimes.

Before I left I kissed the baby and, on an impulse, grabbed the icon, telling myself I was in more need of it than *she* could ever be.

As I crossed the cellar's gloom towards the stuck-open door, I called out in my real voice, 'Hello? Is there anybody there? Hello? I don't mean you any harm, or your baby.' But I met no one, not even outside, where the rain kept on falling, cold and unfeeling, more relentless than ever.

I chose a shed some thirty metres up the village lane, with a clear view of the cellar entrance, and settled down to wait, cushioned by my rucksack. I wanted to see the owner of that purple stiletto and the icon that was now in my pocket, wanted to find out why she had brought her baby to such a godforsaken place.

After a bit the rain eased off. The light began to fade and dusk came drifting down like smoke, softening the ruined aspect of the houses. I could feel the broken skin on my wrists tighten and pucker into new folds. I was healing too quickly.

I'd been waiting three quarters of an hour, getting worried sick about the baby, when I saw the ghost cat glide out the door. It hesitated a moment, lifted its head to sniff the air, then set off up the lane. A few minutes later it was back and again stood sniffing. As I watched I heard an odd rustling sound and suddenly a bird of mythical proportions flapped past the shed – and just as suddenly transformed itself into a young woman, thin and scraggly-looking under a stiff plastic sheet with a slit for her head. She was carrying two rusty buckets. One of her trouser legs hung in tatters round her shin. She was limping badly.

I held my breath and watched. It felt good to be the hunter for once, not the hunted.

The plastic poncho scraped loudly against the door as the bird-woman went through the opening, followed by the Russian Blue. Then nothing. Then a scream, muffled at first. And then she came rushing out with the baby in its blanket, her face a pale disk that reflected the last of the light, her mouth and eyes vague smudges. Hair flying, plastic flapping, she half-limped, half-ran downhill, shrieking, stumbling, barely catching herself when she tried to glance back over her shoulder. She looked just like another maniac escapee from the puke-pastel building behind the mountains, ready for a calming shot from the White Coats. What the hell was she scared of? I'd only taken the icon; I hadn't hurt a hair on her child's head.

Then I remembered about the blood: my blood on the wall of the storeroom and maybe on the baby's cheeks, too.

'Hey, you! Stop! Don't be afraid!'

But she'd already vanished behind one of the ghost houses.

I gave chase – down the ghost lane of the ghost village, into the deepening twilight of a chestnut grove that seemed the only living, growing thing for miles around.

A few metres into the small wood the bird-woman tripped again, stumbled for the last time and pitched forward with a thud, only just managing to twist her body round to protect the baby from the fall. I heard her moan. At my approach she tried wildly to scramble away, clawing at a tree trunk like an animal and half-hauling herself up, spitting at me and shouting things in a guttural language, her voice raw with emotion – before she finally collapsed in a huddle of torn plastic. She lay sprawled and still, without a whimper, shielding the baby that had begun to mewl quietly, as if under its breath, shielding it from me – *me*, of all people! One of her legs was exposed and a bone stuck out from her shin like the splintered end of a skewer. It looked so crazily unreal I started to giggle. Then I gagged.

Next morning, a grey, drizzly, miserable sort of day, I was on a mountain track leading up towards the Maloja Pass again, feeling ragged and a little light-headed from lack of sleep. I had no idea how I'd got there. The rucksack dragged on my back. My glasses and cap were gone; my tongue kept wetting my lips, bare and vulnerable without the moustache; my breasts, released from their bandage, swung free under an unfamiliar black sweatshirt. I must have ditched my Neumann disguise during the night. The bird-woman, the baby and the cat with the luminous eyes were far away, just three more fragments of someone else's memory left to haunt the abandoned settlement.

Around midday I reached the ruins of an old Roman watchtower in the woods somewhere below the summit and sat down for a rest. My lunch consisted of some hardened cheese and a few stale crackers from my rucksack. No more bread for me, ever, not since that trip to the baker's which cost me my child. No more Lord's Prayer either. No more White Coats with syringes, trying to convince me that bread has nothing to do with flesh, the dead flesh of an infant who'd managed to crawl to the bathroom and put her head inside a plastic shower cap…

I was gazing at the icon when I felt something flick against the back of my legs. I looked. Then leapt up cursing the White Coats and their cocktails. But the Russian Blue was still there – crouching at a safe distance now – its magic blue fur, exaggerated whisker pads and green almond eyes quite unmistakeable. And even though I told myself that I had done nothing wrong, I felt another of those flashes of unease.

I tried to ignore the cat stalking me like a shadow, tried to ignore its plaintive, intermittent miaows and the soft stealth of its paws on the pine needles. In the end I jumped across a fast-flowing stream – cats hate water, simple as that. I sighed with relief.

Ten minutes later there was a rustle in the undergrowth. The green stare was almost human – reproachful, angry-hurt.

By mid-afternoon I'd had enough. Under cover of some trees near the village of Maloja, I trimmed my hair with the Swiss Army knife, rolled a large handkerchief into a headband, lined my eyes with Bernhard Neumann's eyebrow pencil, pinched some colour into my cheeks and, hey presto, I'd turned into one of those fortyish women with a still-youthful glow to their skin, discreet makeup, hair cropped rakishly short under a pirate-style scarf, ready to cadge a lift from any passing motorist.

I was picked up by a local in a Range Rover who drove like the devil. The Russian Blue was left behind in a cloud of hellfire exhaust fumes – perhaps it had never existed, after all, except in those blurred reaches of my mind.

The driver had wiry grey hair and the leathery skin of a part-time farmer, part-time ski-lift operator. His brown eyes lacked definition, as if they'd been melted by the Alpine sun. He was smoking a pipe and had the radio on, a Romansch station. I was glad there was no need for small talk. Then the news came on. That's when the man started muttering to himself, his words slurred by the pipe between his lips. At first I didn't pay any attention. Until I realised he was talking in Swiss German, not Romansch.

'Good riddance,' he kept repeating, 'good riddance, yes.' All at once he slowed down, removed the pipe and cocked his head at me, 'What do you think?'

'Excuse me?' I smiled nervously, my fingers clenching the penknife in my pocket.

'Illegal immigrants, I said. We've got enough foreigners in this country already, haven't we? Buying up all our good land, agricultural land at that, for their goddamn holiday chalets. So who's to complain if one or two of them get rubbed out occasionally, eh?'

He speeded up again and I loosened my grip on the knife. But then, suddenly, I felt a cold wind blowing right through me, like I was a kite made of rice paper, glue and balsa wood, at the mercy of the weather and some invisible hand, far below.

'It's all for the better,' the man kept saying.

I nodded feebly, shaken by that icy gust out of nowhere, nameless and quite beyond my understanding.

A week later I was sitting in a restaurant in the Lower Engadine, reading the paper. On the front page was the picture of the bird-woman, not dishevelled now but rather pretty, with high cheekbones and big eyes. Someone, apparently, had given the police an anonymous tip-off, saying there was an injured woman up in the mountains. When she was rescued, she'd reported a man with glasses and a moustache who had pursued her and tried to wrench the child from her arms. A phantom, the police maintained. A ruse to escape the murder charges they were bringing against her. Because, yes, they *had* found a man. A man without glasses or moustache – and he was dead. Cause of death: a brain haemorrhage after a severe blow to the head, probably from a rock. The woman had every reason to hate that man, it seemed. He'd trafficked her into Italy from Ukraine and exploited her as a prostitute for years.

Glancing out the open back door into the shadows of the restaurant garden, I took a sip of coffee and told myself that although she'd been put into prison, the bird-woman was at least safe. And her baby, too. Whatever had happened, they were both safe now. Just like me. I was proud of myself – I'd managed to leave the child behind and bury my hopes of ever being a mother.

I had another sip, then slid the newspaper up on the table to gaze at the icon concealed on my lap. Crude as it was, the love it expressed made my eyes water yet again and I touched a finger to the golden halo around the two figures, to draw strength. Feeling the faint ridge between the different layers of paint, I caught myself thinking, What if the bird-woman shouldn't be in prison at all? What if it should be *me*? Not that I had any recollection of committing a crime. Of attacking a man. Only a vague impression of someone unshaven, with a strong nose and full lips. Just like the victim's face in the grainy newspaper photo in front of me. And just like my husband had looked when I last dreamed of him, months and months ago.

One day, I promised myself as I finished my coffee, one day I would visit the bird-woman in prison. Maybe I would even return the icon to her.

From the restaurant garden came a sudden soft patter, more like an echo in my ears, then there was a flash of silvery blue, so fast I still can't be sure it was real.

Hannah Adcock

A Dislocated Life: Flora MacDonald

Flora MacDonald has become an essential part of the romantic Jacobite legend. She is the heroine to Bonnie Prince Charlie's hero, risking her life to help him escape from the murderous forces of King George II and his fat son, 'Butcher' Cumberland. She is remembered as young and beautiful, tossed on the wild waters between Skye and Benbecula with the Prince, disguised as her maid, gallantly offering her what protection he could against the elements. It is almost impossible not to think of her without humming snippets of 'The Skye Boat Song'.

However, it is less well known that Flora and her fellow Highlanders played a starring role in another doomed political enterprise only thirty years later, this time fighting for the King in America. Of course, it is surprising that staunch rebels had become ardent Loyalists in such a relatively short space of time, but perhaps even more surprising was that Scots, devoted to their ancestral land, were emigrating at all. The migration of the Scottish Highlanders had reached such alarming proportions by the 1770s that Samuel Johnson, visiting in North Britain, could speak of an 'epidemick desire of wandering which spreads its contagion from valley to valley.'

Flora and her husband, Allan MacDonald, set sail for North Carolina in 1774. Her handwritten account of her family's emigration is stored in the National Library of Scotland, where the manuscript will form part of the summer exhibition, *The Original Exports: Stories of Scottish Emigration*. The style and content are evocative, capturing Flora's brave stoicism and her intense mental and physical suffering. It was to be a sad episode for Scotland's ageing heroine.

In the nineteenth and earlier twentieth century the mass emigration of Highlanders had been largely attributed to political causes: John P. Maclean wrote in *Historical Account of the Settlements of Scotch Highlanders in America* (1900) that, 'This emigration, forced by royal persecution and authority, was carried on by those who desired to improve their conditions, by owning the land they tilled.' This was certainly a palatable and even plausible view – that Scots were forced out by the policies of the vengeful British government – but it is probably not the full story. In her excellent book, *The Highland Scots of North Carolina, 1732–1776,* Duane Meyer points out that eighteenth century British observations primarily cited non-political reasons: the changes in agriculture that produced rack rents and evictions; the decay of the clan system even before the '45 that removed the social ties and restraints that might have prevented migration, and the growth of population, contributing to poverty and unrest.

Writing in the third person, Flora McDonald recounts that she 'followed her husband to North Carolina where a great many of the Clan were obliged to go, not being able to pay the rents demanded of them.' An Inverness-shire tacksman, America bound, voiced a common complaint in 1773 that his rent had risen fourfold from £5 to £20 in the twenty years prior to his emigration. Allan MacDonald was also unfortunately placed as a tacksman, whose traditional role of marshalling men for the clan chief, in return for preferential treatment in terms of rent and land rights, had been rendered redundant by the post-'45 legislation of the British government and the new system of land leasing that had no room for middlemen who creamed off a clan chief's assets. Allan was also not the most successful of tacksmen: he was dismissed from his post in 1767, but allowed to stay on at Kingsburgh, the family home, at a greatly increased rent.

As Hugh Douglas writes in *Flora MacDonald: The Most Loyal Rebel*, 'Skye remained an unhappy island of which one tacksman spoke for all when he described it as a Gehenna of misery, a place of torment from which families were being driven because they could not pay the chief's high rents.' On the Isle of Skye in 1774 the people performed a dance called America, 'each of the couples successively whirls round in a circle, till all are in motion; and the dance seems intended to show how emigration catches till a whole neighbourhood is set afloat.'

Flora does not write about how she feels leaving the country of her birth. Only the phrase 'obliged to go' hints at her resistance, and also her powerlessness in the face of such implacable economic and social forces. However, it was not all bad, or at least not immediately. Flora writes that, 'Her husband purchased a plantation with the stock of different cattle thereon, on which they lived comfortably for near a year,' but doesn't go into detail, for it must have been bitter to recall what had once seemed so hopeful. Despite his financial embarrassment, Flora's husband, Allan, had managed to squirrel away enough funds to allow him to purchase a purchase a plantation of 475 acres, of which 70 acres were already clear. There was a fine home on the plantation, as well as three orchards, a barn, storehouse, kitchen, stable, corn crib, and gristmill. Allan brought five indentured male servants and three indentured female servants and valued the furniture, books, and silver in the home at £500.

Flora was accorded a promising welcome to her new homeland, although sources differ as to the degree of rapture extended to the Jacobite heroine. At the Cape Fear settlement, where her family settled, she was close to friends and family, with Gaelic spoken and certain Highland customs maintained. However, despite these traits, North Carolina was a very different place from her island birthplace. It was an area of hills, short ridges and undrained depressions bordering on the upper Cape Fear River and its tributaries. The weather could be blisteringly hot and different farming techniques were needed to cope with the multitude of trees. Different nationalities also formed a substantial part of the settlement, making it much more cosmopolitan than eighteenth-century Skye. However, as Flora writes, she had only a year of peace and hope:

When the American Rebellion brock out, and Congress forcing her husband to joyne them, being a leading man among the highlanders, and seeing he would be obliged to joyne either party, he went in disguise to Fort Johnston on the mouth of the River Capefear, and there settled the plan of riseing the Highlanders in arms, with Governor Martin.

Again, she gives this sense of being powerless in the face of huge forces, forced to participate in a war, obliged to choose sides once more. But why did her family throw in their lot with King George III?

Douglas suggests that Flora and Allan had seen first hand the military might of the Hanoverians and reasoned that, 'What the Redcoats had done in Scotland in 1745–46 they could repeat in America in 1775.' Once it became obvious that they would have to take sides, they were effectively forced into supporting what they assumed would be the winning side. Governor Martin certainly employed both stick and carrot tactics: the stick side leading him to proclaim that people who refused to stand with the monarch might well discover, 'their lives and properties to be forfeited'. The carrot side involved promising land grants to Highlanders who would swear an oath of loyalty to the King and fight for him.

Douglas goes on to suggest that, 'Allan MacDonald's position was further affected by the fact that he had sworn loyalty to King George in order to obtain his commission in the militia', as well as that Allan was faced with another powerful, if considerable less noble inducement. From the moment he arrived in Carolina, Governor Martin has accepted him as a chief of the clansmen: Allan was 'hugely flattered by all this attention and threw in his lot with the Loyalists immediately'.

There is considerable speculation amongst historians as to why Highlanders like Flora and Allan took the side of the King. It is an interesting, if complex debate. Had Allan and Flora had been in America for too little time to really appreciate the reasons behind the rising? Was it significant that Highland attitudes towards the British government and the King had slightly mellowed? Prime Minster Pitt was able to say about Highland soldiers who had fought in the Seven Years' War, 'They did not disappoint my expectations, for their fidelity was equal to their valour.'

Whatever the reason for the MacDonalds throwing their lot in with the King, it was a decision that was probably only made after hours, days, even months of heart searching, as armed conflict became ever more inevitable. The convolutions of Flora's syntax seem to show that she found an explanation difficult, even at a later date.

War and battles finally caught up with the MacDonalds, as Flora writes, presumably drawing on information provided by friends and family, for she did not see the battle first-hand:

haveing no arms, but 600 old bad firlocks, and about 40 broad swords the gentlemen had, and after marching 200 miles, and driveing the enemy from two different posts they had taken, made a night attack on Generall Easwell at the head of 3000 Congrass troops, who were intrenched on the other side of Moors Creek, the bridge being cutt down excepting the two side beams, on which a number of the highlanders got over, but were bet back with considerable lose, the enemy haveing 3 piece of cannon planted in front close to the bridg, which forced the highlanders to retire back 12 miles, to the place from whence they marched the night before. The common highlanders then parting with my husband, Mr McDonald of Kingsborrow, and their other leaders, excepting about ninty faithfull followers, who with their leaders made their way back to Smiths Ferrie on the higher part of Capefear, where Col: Martin with 3000 Congress men mett them, surrounded them & made them prisoners, Mr. McDonald and about 30 other gentlemen were dragged from goal to goal for 700 miles, till lodged in Philadelphia Goal, remaining in their hands for 18 months befor exchanged.

This time, it was Flora's husband rather than herself who was imprisoned for his role in supporting the 'enemy'. The Battle of Moore's Creek Bridge had been a disaster for the Loyalist Highlanders – a second Culloden. Although the Patriots lost only a couple of men, the Highlanders lost fifty, whilst nine hundred Loyalists were rounded up in the next few days, including Allan. Trapped in a region that seethed with hostility towards Loyalists, not knowing what was to become of her husband and eldest son, Flora was desperately unhappy:

> Mrs. Flora McDonald, being all this time in misery and sickness at home, being informed that her husband and friends were all killed or taken, contracted a severe fever, and was deeply oppressed, with stragling partys of plunderers from their army, and night robbers, who more than once threatened her life wanting a confession where her husbands money was. Her servants deserting her, and such as stayed grew so very insolent that they were of no service or help to her. When she got the better of her fever, she went to visit & comfort the other poor

gentlewomen whose husbands were prisoners with Mr. McDonald, as they blamed him as being the author of their misery in riseing the highlanders, and in one of those charitable visits, fell from her horse and brock her right arm, which confined her for months, the only phishitian in the collony being prisoner with her husband in Philadelphia Goal, havening no comforter but a young boy her son, the oldest, Alexr., being prisoner with his father. She remained in this deplorable condition for two years, among robers and faithless servants.

It is interesting that Flora made a point of visiting other 'gentlewomen' whose husbands were also imprisoned. It cannot have been an easy task, given that many of them held her husband responsible for their disastrous condition. It was a lonely time for her, ill and uncertain, with 'no comforter' but her young son. Again, she had to draw on her strength of character to endure, as she had before when she was imprisoned for her part in the Jacobite rising, and had no idea whether she would be sentenced to death, kept prisoner for years or released. In effect, she was as miserably imprisoned as her husband, for a prison doesn't always need bars or physical boundaries to be effective. Her reprieve came two years later, although it was only temporary in nature. The threat of thieves and enemies was soon replaced by other dangers – sea storms and the freezing Canadian winter:

her husband, and son in law, Major Alexr. McLeod, obtained a flag of truce from Sir Henry Clinton and Admirall How, which brought me, my daughter, and her children from Wilmingtown in N: Carolina to New York in the dead of winter, being in danger of our lives for the most of the voyge by a constant storme. I remained for some time at New York, where my husband commanded a company of gentleman volunteers, all Scotsh refugees from Carolina & Virginia. With them (all dressed in scarlet & blew) he and my son Alexr. As Lieutenant, did duty under Generall James Robertson, untill ordered to joyne the 84th Regt. in Nova Scotia, where he & son had got commissions. I was obliged tho tender to follow, and was very nigh deaths door, by a violent disorder the rough sea and long passage had brought on. At last landing in Halifax, were allowed to stay there for eight days on account of my tender state. The ninth day sett off for Windsor, on the Bey of Minas, throw wood & snow and arived the fifth day. There we continued all winter and spring, covered with frost & snow, and almost starved with cold to death, it being one of the worst winters ever seen there, a detachment of the Regiment being there, and by ane accedentall fall next summer, I dislockated the wrist of the other hand, and brock some tendons, which confined me for two months, altho I had the assistance of the regimentall surgeon.

Sick almost to death of her adopted homeland, Flora turned her eyes back towards Scotland. Recent suffering must have dulled the past horrors of her experiences in Skye, and perhaps she still clung on to happy memories of helping the bonny Prince and those first relatively carefree years of married life. She set sail on the *Lord Dunmore* in October, although the voyage was not without incident:

in our passage spying a sail, made ready for action, and in hurreying the ladys below to a place of safety, my foot sliping a step in the trap, fell and brock the dislockated arm in two. It was sett with bandages over slips of wood, and keep my bed till we arrived in the Thames.

Flora had taken charge of the ladies, trying to help them towards relative safety. She had suffered as a result, for she was no longer the young, sprightly lass of '45. Instead, she was becoming an old woman, lines of care and sickness etched on her face. It was Victorian fancy only that pictured her standing proud and defiant on deck, helping to inspire the sailors.

Tragically, her troubles, even then, were not over, for she learnt soon after arriving in Britain that two of her sons, Alexander and Ranald, had been lost at sea in separate incidents. She was devastated.

Those melancholy strocks, by the death of my children who, had they lived, with Gods asistance, might now be my support in my declined old age, brought on a violent fitt of sickness, which confined me to my bed in London for half a year, and would have brought me to my grave, if under Gods hand Doctor Donald Munrow had not given his friendly assistance. The cast in both my arms are liveing monuments of my sufferings & distressis, and the long goal confinment which my husband underwent has brought on such disorders that he has totally lost the use of his legs.

Allan returned to Skye in 1785 with only a small recompense from the British government for all the land and wealth that he'd lost fighting for the King in America, and an income amounting to half his army pay. Of the eleven years that he had been away he had spent fewer than three years with Flora. Their younger son, John, who had been left in the care of a family friend and later posted to Sumatra as a surveyor, provided the only glimpse of better days for the family. By 1787 he had risen through the colonial ranks and amassed enough money to be able to relieve his parents of their financial worries. Still, Flora was weighed down by a sense of futility and failure and ends her narrative with undisguised bitterness:

> I may fairly say we have both suffered in our person, family, and interest, as much if not more than any two going under the name of refugees or loyallists, without the smallest recompence.

The NLS summer exhibition *The Original Exports: Stories of Scottish Emigration* runs from 26 June to 10 October. Extracts from Flora MacDonald's manuscript memoir of her experiences in North Carolina are reproduced with the permission of the Trustees of the National Library of Scotland.

Bernard Pearson

The Isle of Arran

A storm-fire sea
heaves our ferry into
an uneven land.
On the risen ground red deer
like aldermen robed for council
ship across an undercoat of sky

while in the peppered broth
as the tide takes its turn
seals recline like old aunts
in bean-bags; their souls
suddenly akimbo.

To the south of Brodick,
past a swell of pretty pine
and sandy lamentations,
up and round and on we go
to Catacol Bay,
to sit, watch and remember,
how heaven spends her day.

The Man in the Woods

Have you seen the tent
spewed onto the edge of our golf course?
There is someone living there you know
they call him 'Mouth Morgan',
for he is mute

If he could speak
he'd tell you about watching Buster Crabbe
for sixpence and skinning girls from their stockings
and haggling for fags with this weeks uncle.
He'd tell you how In his tent
he keeps a duffel bag, full of 1963.

After which you would be told:
how Jesus had come into his life,
riding on a tiger. and about the time a man
called Nigel brought him other people's shoes
and blankets, dog-eared pages,
scrawled over by unknown lovers,
quicksilvered by desire.

Under trees among scuttling things
where all is whispered, he feels at home,
with a fine new tin opener and socks
dangling over the fire as if it were
that Christmas in Treorchy.

Now Showing

A boy as thin
as Parma ham
dives from the multiplex.
He is not to be consoled.
Tears fall against his
grey translucent skin,
a girl rubs his hair;
she looks so old!

People who go to the cinema
to get away from it all
stare into the middle distance
but then like children licking cake
spoons, they guiltily
look back at the fold-away child.
The neighing ambulance arrives and men dressed
like gas fitters gently place *the bread which we break*
into their removals van.

Catherine Czerkawska

Civil Rights

She liked everything about the city, from the scent of fresh coffee and yeast buns that drifted out of Bewley's in the mornings, when she passed it on her way to work, to the sluggish Liffey reflecting the lights by night. She loved the quiet gallery where, on her days off, she could stand and stare at the jewelled panels of Harry Clarke's stained glass. She loved the smoky pubs and the voices of the people, those hard-edged tones that were the same in all big cities where people had once had to make themselves heard above the din of machinery and traffic and politics.

But if she loved Dublin, she hated her work, a vacation job found for her by one of her father's colleagues. She worked in a gloomy office, its windows so high that you couldn't see out of them. The company dealt in animal feedstuffs and she sat at a desk in a room full of other girls. On each desk was a clumsy calculator that regurgitated a strip of flimsy paper. She would type tons, hundredweights, pounds and ounces into it. Then came prices in pounds, shillings and pence. And then she would do arithmetic and fill in complicated forms. It was 1969 and computerised calculators, if they existed at all, were so large that they filled rooms. Girls came cheaper.

Afterwards, it struck her that she must have got many of the calculations wrong. The job was so boring that getting the calculations wrong seemed like a necessity, staving off misery with small acts of revolution. She sat at the back and worked away with every appearance of diligence, and a man with a grim face sat in front, facing them, like a schoolmaster at his desk, watching them. If they talked he would shout at them, but she seldom talked to anybody and never got shouted at. She was an incomer and largely ignored. She didn't mind too much. She just got on with creating arithmetical mayhem, and left at the end of the day for the hostel up at St Stephen's Green, with its vapid statues in every alcove. It was part of a convent and it was run by the nuns. No men were allowed in the building, never mind in any of the rooms. Sometimes she would get dressed up and go out for the evening with the girls from her shared room and sometimes she would wander about the city all by herself.

Then, a few weeks into her summer, she saw a poster advertising a civil rights meeting in the centre of Dublin. The year before, her first year at university, she had started going to Irish civil rights meetings in Edinburgh. Everyone associated with the movement seemed to have a certain glamour about them, whether it was the handsome professor, who told them about Irish History, or passionate Bernadette Devlin, or the friend of a friend who talked casually about the state of affairs at home and how something had to change sooner or later and it might as well be now. On her way to Dublin, she had travelled through Larne and Belfast. It seemed – as it undoubtedly was – another country, with its big bright King Billy murals and its Union flags everywhere. She had never seen so many flags in all her life.

That Saturday in Dublin, she went to the meeting and mingled with the crowd. She listened to speeches, and felt as if she was part of something meaningful and exciting. Somebody tapped her on the shoulder and when she turned round she saw that it was the friend of a friend from university. There were three of them, big, bold young men. They told her they had come down from the north and when they said that, they grinned at each other with a conspiratorial air. They said they couldn't go back over the border just yet, because things were very hot for them up there. Things would be a bit safer for them down here. They hoped. People noticed their accents, their northern voices and stared at them.

Later, the speeches grew more inflammatory, and the police who were lurking around the edges of the crowd became uneasy. Before the afternoon was over, the *gardai* had baton charged the crowd and people were running in all directions and screaming but she was safe enough because the boys from the north were much more watchful than the innocents from the south. They could see what was developing, could see what was about to happen and before the *gardai* made their move, one or them had seized her hand and said 'run!' They ran with her, pulling her down side streets, and they didn't seem to be afraid, in fact they were laughing as though it were a bit of a joke, not the real thing at all.

They went into a restaurant somewhere down by the river, a good restaurant, busy and full of tourists. They sat there, the three northerners and herself, and she saw that it wasn't the kind of restaurant she could ever afford to go to – her parents maybe, once in a while, but not herself on her student grant. She wondered who would pay, but she still belonged to an age when the man usually paid, especially if he was older, although not perhaps if he was a student. So she thought that they might pay for her, and if they didn't, then she had just enough money in her purse to pay for herself, if she was very careful what she ate, looking at the prices on the menu and choosing the cheapest things. One of the three was a big red-headed, raw-boned man, older than the others, and he wore dark glasses. Even in the restaurant, he didn't take them off and she noticed that he had bruises on his face. When he had tried to run, he had hobbled a bit, and the others had been laughing at him, saying, 'Come on Liam, move your arse!' He sat opposite her and smiled at her, but he had a broken tooth and he looked as though he was in pain. She felt very sorry for him.

'What happened?' she asked and the others frowned, but he told her that he had been beaten up, on his way home from a civil rights meeting, said that they must have been lying in wait for him, he hadn't stood a chance even though he was a big man and quite strong. But they had jumped him, three of them, and although he had managed to inflict a few bruises of his own, they had got him down in the end and kicked him where he lay. After that, they had decided to come over the border because things were looking a bit too hot to handle in the north. But Cork was where they ought to be, he said, not Dublin. Cork was the place to be, and she wondered why.

She knew Cork well, had worked in West Cork as an au pair, the summer when she was sixteen. 'Why Ireland?' somebody had asked and she had said it was because her grandmother was Irish which seemed reason enough. She thought of the place chiefly as a warren of fuchsia fringed lanes, mostly leading down to the sea. She had been looking after two-year-old triplets for an Irish family. They were holidaying in a flat in a run down farmhouse. The rooms were dusty and her bed, in what had once been the maids' quarters, was lumpy and uncomfortable. Mice partied in the attics all night long. The little girls were funny and sweet but difficult. You could walk about with one under each arm, but then you would have to stagger after the third, who was always toddling off somewhere with great determination. Besides, there was a pig that would come crashing through the overgrown gardens, baring its yellow teeth, scaring the life out of you. The farmer's wife, Mary, took a liking to her and would invite her into the big kitchen for tea. She would cut thick slices of corny bread, made with flour and soda and dried fruit, buttering the cut end of the loaf first, holding it in close against her chest and sawing at it with the bread knife. Her nana had made the same thing and cut it in the same dangerous way but she had called it teacake.

When the girls were asleep, she would go out to the dancing in the village. A long driveway threaded through the neglected gardens of the house, between a profusion of buddleia flowers that drooped in the soft rain. For ever afterwards, she could never smell the honey scent of buddleia without remembering a boy called Michael who had kissed her on the driveway in the dark. All these things came into her mind at once, the scents and sounds and the remembrance of physical pleasure, when the red headed man talked about Cork. But she couldn't see why Cork was the place to be. 'A good place,' repeated the red headed man. 'Plenty of the lads down there.'

Not long after this, they got up from the table. One of them told her to head for the door, so she did, expecting that he would pay, wondering if she should offer to give him the money for her meal. But when they got to the door, the red headed man took her hand and said 'now we run!' and yanked her almost off her feet. Then they were running down the stairs and out into the street, and the other two were running after. They didn't stop until they were many streets away, leaning on each other and laughing. She was genuinely shocked and afterwards, for the rest of her time in the city, worried about it, worried that somebody would recognise her, wondered if she should go in and offer to pay, but it seemed an impossibility. Not her fault. And so she just let it go.

After that, they got a taxi, all chipping in for the fare. It stopped outside an old stone building that seemed to be divided into flats. They went up a narrow stair and knocked on a door. After a muttered conversation between the friend of a friend and somebody inside they were admitted to a shabby room. There was an ordinary wooden table and the smell of petrol was in the air, sickly and strong. She saw that the table was stacked with ranks of glass lemonade and wine bottles and funnels, like when her dad made wine on the kitchen table, but the bottles were full of something else. There were pieces of paper stuffed into the necks of them and trailing down the sides. She should have been afraid but she wasn't. There was an odd sort of excitement about it. But they didn't stay there long.

'Not safe,' the red-headed man said. 'They don't know what they're doing. And besides I need a smoke.' So they went out of the flat and down the stone stairs that smelled of pee and potatoes, and all the time they took her with them, as though she were one of them, as though she were part of the group. But still none of it seemed in any way real. Afterwards, when she came to look back on it, it was as if she had been watching a character in some art house film. And then they were walking through the empty streets of the city, which was very art house as well, and a thin rain was starting. The red headed man in his suit that was dusty and creased, as though he had slept in it one too many nights, pulled on the very end of his cigarette like a drowning man sucking in air and said 'Oh shit.' She said that she would have to go because the nuns locked the doors of the hostel before midnight. The friend of a friend said – as if the idea had just occurred to him – 'maybe we could hire a car between us or borrow one and you could drive us down to Cork.'

Taken aback, she said, 'But I can't drive. I haven't learnt yet.'

The red-headed man, with his bruised face, who had suddenly bent double because the deep breathing seemed to have hurt his ribs, stood upright again and pulled off his glasses, and she could see that he had two black eyes, all bruised and raw with the whites shot through with red veins. He put out his hand and took hold of her arm, and stared at her, really stared at her. She felt a frisson of something that might have been fear or pity or something else altogether.

How old *are* you? he asked.

'I'm eighteen,' she said, and he said, 'Sweet fucking Jesus Christ almighty! I thought you were twenty-five at least.' He looked at his friend and said 'what is she *doing* here? What the fuck is she *doing* here?'

The friend shrugged. She realised that she was very frightened. There was a pause, a space of a few seconds, then the red headed man sighed and shook his head. He took her gently by the shoulders.

'Listen to me. Go home now. This is not for you,' he said.

He turned and walked off down the empty street. He seemed very angry all of a sudden. They followed him, the friend of a friend remonstrating with him. She trailed after them feeling faintly embarrassed, and they walked until they were back on Grafton Street.

'You know your way from here?' asked the friend of a friend.

'Yes, but what about him?'

'He'll be fine. Won't you Liam?'

The red-headed man turned towards her but he had put his sunglasses back on again and she couldn't see his eyes. His smile was a grimace.

'Oh yes,' he said. 'I'll be as right as rain. You go home now. Go home.'

She went back to the hostel. She was almost late. A tight-lipped nun was waiting in the hall, rattling a bunch of keys. There was a marble font of holy water to one side of the door.

'Goodnight, sister,' she said.

She dipped her hand into the water, crossed herself, and went up to bed.

Will Brady

Homecoming 2009

Thanks to a Scottish Government initiative, 2009 has been designated Scotland's year of 'Homecoming': a celebration of everything Scottish to which we are all, apparently, invited. In his introduction to the official Events Guide, Alex Salmond, MSP and First Minister of Scotland, reminds us that this year marks the 250th anniversary of the birth of 'our national poet and cultural icon' – Robert Burns. Naturally, this is cause for veneration: 'Burns is the inspiration behind our year long celebration of some of Scotland's great contributions to the world: Golf, Whisky, Great Minds and Innovation, Burns himself and our full culture and heritage.'

While we might ponder the semantic curiosity of Burns being the inspiration for a celebration of himself, more troubling is Salmond's choice to cite only golf and whisky as Scotland's crowning achievements, before resorting to the disconcertingly vague 'Great Minds and Innovation', and the transparently floundering 'full culture and heritage'. Salmond's words are, ironically, symptomatic of the reductive and antiquated preconception of contemporary Scotland that he is, presumably, attempting to challenge.

The 'Homecoming Scotland' campaign has been widely criticised, and is, in many respects, an easy target. A *Guardian* blog dismisses the initiative as 'an embarrassing attempt' by the Scottish government and its official tourist agency, VisitScotland, to generate revenue from a tourist population 'with a taste for the conservative and the clichéd'. Certainly, there is an economic motive for the celebrations; Salmond himself confirmed that his intention was to 'spur economic recovery by using Scotland's assets fully and creatively'. The criticism seems to have been levelled not so much at the former ends, as the latter means: the objection is to the relentless perpetuation of kilt-and-bagpipes imagery, which, certainly, is neither a full nor a creative expression of Scottish identity. It is true, however, that 'traditional images of Scotland are... strong in people's minds abroad' and the fact that the Homecoming campaign has been heavily promoted in Canada, New Zealand and Australia would appear to confirm the existence of a globally dispersed population for whom such symbolism resonates. There are some forty million people worldwide who describe themselves as having Scottish links; to cultivate an impulse amongst the Scottish diaspora to 'come home' has the potential to be very lucrative for Scotland's tourist industry.

Except that the campaign's marketing strategy betrays a stubbornly narrow sense not only of Scotland's cultural production, but also of what constitutes an authentically Scottish ethnicity. According to *The Times*, when the government first announced its plans for Homecoming Scotland in June last year, it 'gleefully presented in its publicity material an image of hundreds of happy white-faced "heroes" marching off to celebrate their Scottishness'. Six months later, the image had been conspicuously amended: now, in the front rank of revellers, we see a solitary Asian man, dutifully reading from a collection of Robert Burns's poetry. Officials claimed that this updated image represents 'the diversity of modern Scotland'. Campaigners for racial equality took a rather different view, castigating the change as insulting tokenism. Professor Geoff Palmer, president of the Edinburgh and Lothians Race Relations Council, accused the government of aiming its campaign squarely at wealthy white Americans, and denounced the doctored image as 'a deception'.

Palmer's contempt is understandable, and scandals such as this make easy prey for the media, though generally, discussion of the subject falls short of a thoughtful enquiry into the problems of ethnicity, cultural heritage, and political allegiance in contemporary Scotland. When Salmond writes: 'Whether you're a Scot, you have Scots ancestry or you have a passion for our great nation', it seems pertinent to consider the demographic to which this appeal is being made, and to question, more broadly, the state of contemporary Scottish identity.

This is, nevertheless, as many sociological studies have confirmed, an extremely complex undertaking, and one benighted with paradoxes, misconceptions, and problems of definition. Robin Williams, in his article, *The Sociology of Ethnic Conflicts*, asks, 'How is ethnicity related to "nation" and "nationality"?' Hypothetically, the answer seems straightforward enough: 'A nation is a politically conscious ethny, claiming statehood rights on the basis of common ethnicity… Nationalism is an ideological movement in support of a nation.' In practice, however, this definition runs into difficulties. 'Since few territorial (national) states are populated by a single ethny, the term "nation-state" is muddled and intellectually dangerous'. This is certainly true in the case of Scotland, as Anthony Cohen has pointed out in *Personal Nationalism: A Scottish View of Some Rites, Rights, and Wrongs*, 1996:

> Scotland is a country of enormous heterogeneity in almost every significant social respect. It is ethnically, linguistically, and religiously plural; its population is dispersed through regions that are geographically disparate… its class divisions are as marked as those of anywhere in the modern world. Anyone's Scotland can be substantially different from anyone else's.

This observation foregrounds Cohen's analysis of nationalism in Scotland, and specifically, 'the association that individuals make between themselves and the nation'. The nation is, he suggests, 'one of the resources on which individuals draw to formulate their sense of selfhood', but that 'self-identity is misunderstood if regarded as being determined by, or as derived from, membership of the nation'. Furthermore, by neglecting 'the personal dimension of nationalism, and by thus understating the agency of the self in the construction of the nation, [we] risk misunderstanding nationalism itself'. Evidently, we are on treacherous ground. But, as Cohen is keen to point out, 'the histories, literatures, folklores, traditions, languages, musics, landscapes, and foods of Scotland are social facts on which individuals draw in providing themselves with a shared vocabulary. That is how culture works.' It is in *sharing* that 'the sentiment of and attachment to the nation is predicated'. When put in these terms, we begin to see why Alex Salmond is obliged to construct a picture of Scotland that relies on such tired stereotypes. Cohen again:

The nationalist politician... like any aspiring leader, has to recruit the sympathies of the largest possible number of people by talking to them in terms with which they can all identify. The political nationalist 'collectivises' nationalism, while the individual personalises it.

Salmond is undoubtedly attempting to 'collectivise' nationalism, to incite, even, a nationalistic fervour, and hoping, presumably, to exploit the ideology of a 'putative Scottishness [that] seems to be compelling in contemporary Scotland'. And indeed, beyond. In October last year, Edinburgh University opened a centre for the study of the Scottish diaspora, a department which seeks to investigate the international fascination with Scotland, a 'generally white phenomenon' that is becoming increasingly popular in Germany and Eastern Europe where Highland games and Scottish clubs are reportedly flourishing. This research points to the problem of defining an 'authentic' national identity, and goes some way to explaining why the terms 'blood Scots' and 'heart Scots', as used in the Homecoming literature, have caused both confusion and offence. More problematic still is the tendency for a national allegiance to be formulated in antagonistic terms: that is, for Scottish national identity to be driven by a sense of hostility or opposition to England. This is a problem not only with the construction of Scottish identity, of course, but for the very concept of national identity; it has been argued that *all* identity is contrastive, that indeed, 'this is its very rationale'. Julian Pitt-Rivers, in his 1954 anthropological study of Europe, claimed that it is closest neighbours who most cherish and exploit their differences from each other. Another study concurs:

> While the foundations for nationalist sentiment throughout the world are varied, in Europe the basis has been the boundaries of the nations which gained independent political status in medieval Christendom... In Europe, the normal basis for nationalism is, therefore, in a sense always backward-looking, always advertising to past glories, always apparently more conscious of the past than of the present. (H.M. Begg and J.A. Stewart, *The Nationalist Movement in Scotland*, 1971)

It follows then that the boundary between Scotland and England should have proved so crucial in the provisioning of Scottish – and English

– identities; furthermore, that contemporary political rhetoric should invoke an anachronistic national self-image. And because national identity is 'never so secure and so lacking in ambiguity and ambivalence that is can be left to look after itself,' we find it 'ritualised, mythified, symbolised, and emblematised' (Cohen).

For Scotland, this process seems to have begun with the Union with the English Crown in 1603, followed by the Union of the Parliaments a century later (in 1707), which created the new legal entity of Great Britain. There followed a period of intense socio-economic change: two hundred years of unparalleled prosperity for Scotland, which was largely attributed to the Union, and which for some historians, essentially marked the start of Scottish history because it 'represented the beginnings of material progress for the Scots (and therefore of the cultural and intellectual achievements of the Scottish Enlightenment) and the true origins of the creation of nineteenth-century Greater Britain.' (MacKenzie, *Empire and National Identities: The Case of Scotland*, 1998). If imperialism brought this Greater Britain to fruition, it also helped to establish the terms on which national identities are self-formulated. Inherent is a sense of cultural superiority, which MacKenzie sees as being 'forged out of a reading of history upwards into the realm of myth'.

Scotland's trajectory of mythification owes much to the 'discovery', in the 1760s, of what was claimed as the 'ancient poetry' of a third-century Highland bard named Ossian. Colin Kidd writes:

The Ossianic phenomenon did not seriously disturb the ideological trends engendered by the Scottish Enlightenment; indeed it may have reinforced them. For although the ancient Celtic heroes of the Ossianic poems had many 'refined' qualities, fine feelings and noble sentiments, combined with cultural simplicity, and heroic ferocity in war, were the hallmarks of savagery. Thus Scottish Gaels... contributed very little of substance to Scottish identity after the eighteenth century. (*Gaelic Antiquity and National Identity in Enlightenment Ireland and Scotland*, 1994)

Gaeldom had once enjoyed a privileged role in Scottish political culture; an identity associated with the dark-age kingdom of Dalriada consolidated as Scots between the tenth and thirteenth centuries people of Pictish, British,

Saxon, Norman, Breton, and Flemish descent, as well as the Dalriadic Scots themselves. Not only was this Dalriadic history the basis of national claims to be a sovereign *imperium* independent of the English, religious identity too depended on the Gaelic past, and especially on tales of the mythical Dalriadic king, Donald I. The Dalriadic imagination, however, coexisted in Scotland from the later medieval period with a Lowland critique of Gaelic life and manners, especially of the lawlessness of the Highland clans, though not until the eighteenth century was this practical antipathy towards Gaeldom matched by a rejection of the nation's proud Dalriadic past. Then, according to Kidd:

> Scotland's Celtic identity was dealt a series of intellectual blows from which it never fully recovered... In the works of Scotland's enlightened historical sociologists... the values of her Highland Gaelic culture came to be detached from any special national or ethnic significance, and instead reinterpreted within a temporal framework of human civilization as symptoms of social backwardness.

As far as the literati of Scotland's improving Lowlands were concerned, the Highlands were an embarrassing anachronism; the past, they argued, was a foreign country; 'the mental world of primitive man, including one's own ethnic and national forebears... were far removed conceptually from the concerns of civilized, commercial modernity'. Modernity, thus conceived, is contingent upon a selective reading of history. Enlightened Scots, by minimising ethnic differences in institutions and cultural life, were able to distance themselves emotionally from Scottish Gaeldom as from any primitive society, so that the reinvented Highland culture that emerged in the nineteenth century was but a 'tame accessory to British unionism and imperialism [which] did nothing to restore to Scots a powerful ethno-cultural identity' (Kidd). Murray Pittock, in *The Invention of Scotland*, concurs, seeing 'the romantic signs and symbols' of this Highland culture as key elements in the 'reconciliation of Scottish ethnic nationalism with its global stage' (MacKenzie). But the imperial interaction was also bound up with the securely Lowland Burns tradition and the effort to construct Scottish heroes that combined in their persons both Highland and Lowland characteristics. The problem of Scotland's diverse (and coexisting) cultures could therefore be resolved by contriving an amalgam of elements – as neatly represented by the Burns societies, Highland games, and St Andrews organisations that sprang up around the Empire and persevere to this day.

On 25 January this year, some 1,030 Burns Clubs with 80,000 members in eighteen countries paid tribute to the Bard's anniversary; the sheer scale of the 'Burns Supper' ritual is a testament to his enduring status as Scotland's 'cultural icon'. The persistence of Burns is curious – though it is perhaps appropriate that he should represent a nation whose history, like his own, has been sanitised, mythologised, and sometimes, outright fabricated. As Neal Ascherson observes in a recent article in the *London Review of Books*, Burns enthusiasts have, over the past two centuries, found themselves compelled to 'invent him and reinvent him in one imaginative hagiogram after another'. Distortion of the truth seems permissible, inevitable even, when facts are scarce (or, just as often, contradictory), for in the telling the story of Burns, 'confession that one has no idea why Burns did this or that, or what he thought about him or her, has seemed almost disloyal to the Immortal Memory'. So we have been subjected to 'a procession of biographers dressing their own Burns dolls in their own favourite costumes'.

Robert Burns lived a short, passionate and erratic life, and his behaviour seems often inexplicable. How is it that a staunch advocate of equality and liberty, and author of 'The Slave's Lament', could have considered, at one point, travelling to Jamaica to become a slave-driver? Or that he could mourn the loss of Scottish independence, while praising the British Constitution? It seems, as Ascherson puts it, that from time to time, 'Burns stuffed his principles into the drawer along with some of his best poems'. These inconsistencies are ignored for contemporary purposes of deification; rather, Alex Salmond reminds us that Burn's 'message of friendship, Auld Lang Syne, lives on the world over'.

There is an interesting parallel here to the conventional telling of Scottish history, from which unsavoury details are often omitted – including Scotland's involvement with slavery – or common misconceptions perpetuated, such as the belief that Scotland was conquered by England. The process of 'mythification', of which the Homecoming celebrations are yet another proponent, has worryingly conservative implications. We should perhaps see 2009, not as cause for celebration of predictable Scottish platitudes, but as an opportunity to engage productively with the cultural diversity that has always been central to Scotland's history, and that exists to this day.

Reviews

Homage to Caledonia
Daniel Gray. Luath Press. ISBN 9781906307646. £16.99

The Spanish civil war (1936–39) had a remarkable impact in Scotland. In relative terms, the number that volunteered to fight for the Republic was greater north than south of the border. Approximately 550 Scots would see military action in Spain before General Franco declared victory on 1 April 1939. Yet memories of Spain lived on in Scotland long after Republican defeat: in the early 1960s, Stuart Christie listened to stories of the British Battalion of the XV International Brigade in the mining town of Blantyre. Aged only eighteen in 1964, Christie participated in a failed anarchist plot to assassinate Franco in Madrid.

However, there is surprisingly little written on the Scottish response to the fratricidal conflict in Spain. While Hywel Francis and Robert Stradling have studied the Welsh and the Irish extensively, the best work on the Scots has been Ian MacDougall's oral history of Scottish volunteers, *Voices from the Spanish Civil War* (1986). Daniel Gray, a curator at the National Library of Scotland, has drawn on MacDougall's research in his celebration of Scottish support for the Spanish Republic during the civil war. Not surprisingly, he has also made extensive use of archival papers deposited at the NLS.

Utilising this primary material, Gray tells some astonishing and tragic stories. For example, Jimmy Rutherford from Leith was captured in the battle of Jarama in February 1937 with other members of the British Battalion as they sought to prevent the Nationalist encirclement of Madrid. Tried for the crime of 'military rebellion', Rutherford was sentenced to death before being released as part of a prisoner-exchange. Forced to agree not to return to Spain, he rejoined his comrades in the British Battalion in August 1937. Re-captured in March 1938, he was recognised by one of his original interrogators, and shot two months later when only twenty years old.

Although this book contains fascinating material, much of it could have been written thirty years ago. Gray does not engage with current historiographical debates. He minimises the significance of Catholic workers' hostility towards the Republic caused by the killing of around 7,000 priests, and claims that the labour movement's cautious response to the civil war (which included support for Non-Intervention until 1937) was motivated by electoral concerns. In fact, as Tom Buchanan demonstrated in his 1991 monograph on the British labour movement, Spain represented a clear threat to the close relationship between Catholicism and organised labour; the leadership not only feared that unconditional support for the 'godless' Republic would lose votes but that it would fatally split the movement.

Similarly, Gray's largely hagiographical account of the Scottish Aid Spain movement does not consider Lewis Mates's critique of pro-Republican humanitarianism made in his 2007 book *The Spanish Civil War and the British Left: Political Activism and the Popular Front.* Mates does not deny the organisation and sheer hard work that went into Aid Spain campaigns, but argues that they 'depoliticised' the Spanish issue and obscured the malevolent impact that Non-Intervention was having on the military fortunes of the Republic.

Most importantly, in his treatment of the thorny issue of Communism, Gray does not seem to have consulted studies (such as James Hopkins's seminal 1998 monograph on the British Battalion), that have utilised Comintern files released following the collapse of the USSR in 1991. Emphasising the anti-fascist nature of Communist support for the Republic, there is little on the Stalinisation of the British Battalion and the punishments inflicted on those brigaders who questioned the party line. Thus stories like Alec Marcovitch's, a Communist Jew from the Gorbals who arrived in Spain in October 1937 only to be arrested and imprisoned as a Trotskyist for criticising Soviet anti-semitism, are absent from Gray's narrative.

Unlike George Orwell's *Homage*, this book does not explore the issues at stake in the Spanish civil war. Gray adopts the contemporary pro-Republican interpretation of an international anti-fascist crusade while bizarrely claiming that it is 'the now widely accepted opinion that the Spanish war was not a civil one.' This is symptomatic of the fact that Spaniards only appear at the margins of his narrative as grateful recipients of Scottish military and humanitarian assistance. There is no mention of those Spaniards who fought in the British Battalion despite the fact that some appear alongside Scottish volunteers in photographs reproduced in the book. Such was the importance of Spanish conscripts making up the crippling losses suffered by the British Battalion in 1937, that the *Volunteer for Liberty*, the organ of the English-speaking International Brigades, became bilingual in February 1938.

While the definitive account of Scotland and the Spanish civil war remains to be written, Gray's book will delight those readers, like Tony Benn, who believe that the Republicans fought 'for democracy and socialism'.

Julius Ruiz

Derangements
Rajorshi Chakraborti. Harper Collins. ISBN 9788172237653. Rs295

In his second novel, *Derangements*, Rajorshi Chakraborti spans continents and straddles worlds, mischievously bestowing a shortened version of his own name, Raj Chakraborti, on his main character, an internationally renowned and controversial novelist who has disappeared from public view.

The novel is structured in three parts and Chakraborti includes a spurious editor's note at the beginning to help a reader out: 'pay attention now: this might be useful. You'll find that the chapters alternate between two distinct books, the second of which is clearly fiction. Book One however is a memoir.' Alarm bells immediately start to ring because the earnest insecurity of 'clearly' gives the game away. The distinction between 'fiction' and 'fact' is nowhere near as clear as the luckless editor would like to believe and the third part of the book, an epilogue, complicates matters further. The author's ex-wife attempts to set the record straight, at least as she sees it, by challenging an important pillar of her ex-husband's 'real-life' story.

But whose voice to trust? Raj Chakraborti may be a famous author, 'beloved and controversial in equal measure,' but he also comes across as an emotionally sterile, complacent and self-centred weakling. What's worse, the police want to question him about the murder of a young journalist whom he was the last person to have met. Raj's fictional creation, on the other hand, 'the perfect worker,' otherwise called Charles Robert Pereira, is a psychopathic killer, controlled by shadowy puppeteers from the higher echelons of business and government. Chakraborti gives Charles the brilliant opening line, 'Every year I used to commit a murder.'

Raj's wife, Ana, is a successful film director, described, at least by her husband, as a 'promiscuous siren'. And what about the author himself? Perhaps calling his main character by his own name helps Chakraborti pull a few satirical punches to do with the role of the author in society, or to play off a few in-jokes, but for the most part Raj and Rajorshi are very different, because the famous author is rootless to the point of insanity, whilst his creator, I suspect, is not. More obviously, the one is fictional, the other real, for even in playful novels it's always possible to make such distinctions.

Chakraborti himself, or at least his restless intellect, can perhaps be traced more profitably through various world-view speeches, which probe 'all-encompassing alliances' and 'indecipherable interests', that may or may not govern the world. If this sounds like an Agatha Christie novel (perhaps

They Came to Baghdad?), it's for good reason. *Derangements* is, at least in part, a multi-layered mystery and murder story with some political philosophising thrown in for good measure.

The stories of Raj and Charles overlap quite late in the book, although there is always a tension between the two narratives, with their individual twists, derangements and parallel occurrences. This delay could be frustrating if you're looking for a neat story, but if you're prepared to be patient and open-minded – the 'perfect reader' – you'll be amply rewarded by the teasing hints and eventual collisions.

The novel's settings range from Rio de Janeiro to London and Calcutta, although thankfully each destination is signposted below the chapter heading, and each chapter is separated from its precursor by a blank page – to prevent excessive confusion. The young and ill-fated journalist Sharon is also a globe trotter, careering around the world gathering dirt for a book called *The Leap*, which will expose the illegal activities that allow successful business people to make the leap to entrepreneurial superstardom.

This book disappears after her murder – if it ever existed in the first place. Its absence is a key to the novel, for it is as much through what isn't written or seen as what is, that Chakraborti constructs his novel of ideas. He pulls, pushes and pierces the painted veil of real life, teasing a reader to 'discern shadows from ghosts, paranoia from persecution, fiction from actual.'

Derangements is surreal in places and I'm not quite sure that this always works. The last fifth of the book has a distended feeling as pace and tension give way to the nether regions of imagination and symbolism. The surrealism of the first instalment of Book Two, by contrast, is invigoratingly tense, for although the story is surreal, the language itself is calm and realistic.

Derangements confirms Chakraborti as an ambitious writer, bravely traversing vast spaces, literal and metaphysical, committed to developing original structures and ideas. His latest work demands much of its reader, but generously rewards the careful, drawing us into a strange, colourful world where mystery, murder, masters of the universe and magical cats all feature. To quote a sentence from the novel: 'The implications were as absurd as they were terrifying, evidence either of a frightening degree of insanity, or worse, of truth!'

Hannah Adcock

Not Just Moonshine: New and Selected Poems
Tessa Ransford. Luath Press. ISBN 9781906307776. £12.99

Religious poetry had a generally hard of time of it as Scotland's twentieth-century got into its stride, partly because the Kirk's grip on cultural permission was so decisively challenged by writers of recent and living memory. The vigorously secular priorities of Hugh MacDiarmid, Sorley MacLean, Norman MacCaig, Iain Crichton Smith, Kenneth White, Edwin Morgan and Douglas Dunn established free-thinking strategies for observation and for structures of feeling liberated from faith-based premises. In this 'Knox-ruined nation', as George Mackay Brown put it, forms of mysticism don't readily find congenial space in historically empiricist soil; and with the exception of Neil Gunn's Zen-inspired fiction, spiritualism or transcendentalism of whatever inclination traditionally gets short shrift.

This major collection of Ransford's poetry, bringing together work from the last four decades along with fifty new poems, appears at a time when change is in the air. Ransford brings a range of speculative religious structures of feeling – from Sufi to Quaker – regularly into play. Born in India, she first discovered Tagore's *Gitanjali* in a Scottish school library. Over the years she has developed an imaginative dialectic where India and Scotland function as complementary opposites in an East-West synthesis of her own making. 'My Indian Self' maps a comparative experience of interior landscapes shaped by radically different cultural climates:

> Let me wear the silks,
> the sandals and the gold.
> Let me dip my fingers
> in the bowl of desire
> even here in the puritan
> corners of my dwelling

As far as life in Scotland is concerned, aspects of Quakerism have proved congenial to Ransford's negotiations of a politics of being in the world, offering a space where ethical imperatives can internalise as forms of social engagement. Her openness to this persuasion goes back to her time as an undergraduate in the 1950s, and exposure to John Macmurray's philosophy classes. A mode of thinking that was sympathetic to Quakerism (Macmurray would later join the Society of Friends) helped her to find bearings; she also learned from his *Reason and Emotion* (1935) that feelings, as much as the intellect, need to be educated. An early piece called 'Poetry of Persons' reads like an oblation of Macmurray's propositions, and 'Epistle' thanks him 'for his lucid word:/ two people are a person when related'.

Ransford freely associates with transcendentalist assumptions, well aware that extensions of the self in a sociable community become largely a matter of language and thus of invention. In 'Epistle' she gives thanks 'for sign and sacrament in every least/ concern or prayer, spilling from the centre/ where God in us and we in God may enter'; and a feminist version of what the American Ralph Waldo Emerson called the unifying 'Oversoul' becomes a coat of many colours Ransford is always ready to wear. Perhaps too ready. 'Epistle' includes the lines:

> I am said God, who needs no predicate.
> Of that great absolute I am revealing
> the whole within myself in tiny part.
> And nothing can detract from that one whit:
> I am beyond all category or sect.
> I, in becoming human, am perfect.

What might satisfy as philosophical/religious aspiration can translate in a poem as unearned declaration, where mantras, spells and incantations run the risk of reducing to homiletics.

Evidently Ransford felt the need for a change in focus if not direction when she made the decision to be less emotional in her poetry and to write as objectively as she could. The first fruits of this determination was *Shadows from the Greater Hill* (1987) where, by recording in diary-form the changing scenes and seasons on and around Arthur's Seat, she exercises her 'wispy, slender, Scottish/ Asian, aching, striding, enduring, joyous, anxious, hopeful/ woman-shape' across a range of moods and reflections. 'February 14th' reignites Edinburgh's extinct volcano in city sunlight and associates it with cross-gendered Indian mythology: 'an elephant-god/ fat, sleek, pregnant' now seen as 'detached from predicaments/ of weather or winter', and a figure who:

> laughingly knows of desire's flame
> never quenched to nirvana,
> but lit anew in rock and sinew
> year by year.

Seven years later, with *Medusa Dozen*, thirteen poems that grew out of a failed relationship become an effective rehabilitation for the feminine intelligence of an ancient symbol of sacred wisdom. In the selection offered in *Not Just Moonshine*, 'Medusa Five' ironises as it vindicates Ransford's assessment of 'this unemphatic,/ non-expectant, poised/ detachment/ I have worked for':

> The man I love is petrified.
> He never looks directly at me now
> or wants to see me. He has weapons
> to destroy me; but I turn
> the other cheek, present my other face.

Colin Nicholson

A Passion for Nature: The Life of John Muir
Donald Worster. Oxford University Press. ISBN 9780195166828. £18.99

If ever the adage about a prophet not being recognised in his own country applied, it would pertain to the passionate nineteenth-century naturalist, John Muir.

In the summer vacation from university in 1953, my parents gave me a twenty-first birthday present of a voyage across the Atlantic in a Donaldson Line 'tub' called the *Lisomoria* and third-class rail tickets by CPR/CNR across Canada. The rest was up to me to earn dollars. With the surplus of my earnings, I took a cheap Greyhound bus journey, spending a few days in the Giant Redwoods. In the communal dining facility, the Americans, hearing that I was a Scot, asked me about John Muir. 'John who?' I responded lamely. Seldom have I been made to feel more ignorant. It was the first time I had ever heard of John Muir. Yet, in California, Oregon, Wyoming, and indeed throughout the US, Muir enjoyed heroic status. His name is indelibly associated with the Sierra Club, which he founded, and which has become one of the most important conservation organisations in North America. Quite simply, Muir's influence on the environmental movements being embraced by President Obama has been huge. Without him, vast swathes of wilderness would not have been saved.

A Passion for Nature is the first comprehensive study of Muir's life based on his extant private correspondence. I was increasingly enthralled as I read the 466 pages, (superbly produced, and printed, as Muir would have been pleased to know, on acid-free paper), by the complex and fascinating human being behind the legend of the solitary mountain man and wilderness hiker. In 2004, my wife Kathleen and I, as the only identified European relations of the 33rd President of the United States, were invited to Independence, Missouri, and Kansas City for the celebrations of the 120th anniversary of Harry Truman's birth. It was from Michael Devine, Director of the Truman Presidential Library, and his senior colleague Liz Sattler, that I first heard the name of Donald Worster, Hall Distinguished Professor of American History at the University of Kansas, who wrote a seminal book, *Dust Bowl: the Southern Plains of the 1930s* which won the prestigious Bancroft Prize. Above excellently researched content, Worster writes elegantly, eloquently, and with great clarity.

What I had not realised before reading *A Passion for Nature* was the extent to which Muir was not only a visionary but a practical 'political' operator.

One crucial milestone was the election year of 1896. The Secretary of the Interior, Hoke Smith, who had the ear of Grover Cleveland, Theodore Roosevelt, and many others at the epicentre of American decision-making, including Harrimans, Mellons and Rockefellers, asked the National Academy of Sciences to recommend policies for all the public forests in the West. The Academy's honorary president, the distinguished, recently retired Wolcott Gibbs jumped at the chance of organising the official commission. Gibbs asked his colleague Charles Sprague Sargent, Harvard professor of botany, and owner of a manor house surrounded by 80 acres of exquisite gardens and a pond, on the outskirts of Boston, to chair the Commission. The other members were William H. Brewer, botanist at Yale and former member of the Whitney Survey in California, General Henry Abbot of the Army Corps of Engineers, Alexander Agassiz, Harvard zoologist, and Arnold Hague, representing the US Geological Survey, and a young practical forester Gifford Pinchot; Gibbs himself was ex-officio. Muir was invited to join this heavyweight group on a grand summer tour of forests in the American West.

Worster describes Sargent as 'thick in girth and severe in manner – but deeply passionate about trees'. Muir got on well with Sargent, to such an extent that Sargent dedicated one of the fourteen volumes in his own classic work, *Silva of North America,* to him. Worster quotes from a letter from Sargent to Muir, about the latter's 1894 book *The Mountains of California.* 'I have never read descriptions of trees that so pictured them to the mind as yours do. No fellow who was at once, a poet, naturalist, and a keen observer has to my knowledge ever written about trees before, and I believe you are the man who ought to have written *Silva of North America.* Your book is one of the great productions of its kind, and I congratulate you on it.'

One of the strengths of Worster's book is that he gives the reader an insight into John Muir as a human being. On his journey east to collect an honorary degree from Harvard, Muir made a stop-over in Wisconsin to see his mother. He found her heart failing and death approaching. What did he do? He told her old Scots stories to cheer her up! An imaginative Scot!

Tam Dalyell

The Bard
Robert Crawford. Jonathan Cape. ISBN 9780224077682. £20.00
Robert Burns: The Patriot Bard
Patrick Scott Hogg. Mainstream. ISBN 9781845964122. £17.99
Robert Burns: A Life
Ian McIntyre. Constable. ISBN 9781845294694. £9.99

Of course, none of these biographies will shock in the way that Catherine Carswell's *Life of Burns* did in the 1930s. When it was serialised by the *Scottish Daily Record and Mail*, it set the heather ablaze. The President of the Burns Federation condemned it, and Carswell received in the post a letter containing a rifle bullet. With it came a message, signed by one 'Holy Willie'. It read, 'use it on yourself and leave the world a better and cleaner place.'

None of our biographers, thankfully, is likely to elicit a similar response from the general reader, though within the academic arena, the gloves are always off. Like grouse on a lek, each of our biographers asserts himself as cock o' the walk: Crawford positions his book as being *the* first twentieth-century biography of our national poet, though Hogg's is as much a contender for that title. Ian McIntyre's, first published in 1995, is now re-issued with a revised final chapter 'to take account of the celebrations planned' for 2009, and asserts that, since the publication of his book, 'there have been no major advances in Burns' scholarship.' On the recent controversy surrounding the 'supposed' authorship of certain poems ascribed by Hogg to Burns, with a seeming sense of great fairness, Crawford writes that he has 'deliberately avoided the arguments that depend on ... discredited scholarship.' Yet by way of this paralepsis, he draws further attention to the matter he appears to wish to avoid discussing. A master-stroke.

Robert Crawford's *The Bard* is principally a literary biography, with the emphasis on the growth of Burns as poet, on his literary achievement and on his legacy. In his introduction, Crawford includes a brief delineation of the history of Burns scholarship, acknowledging the magisterial contribution that David Daiches made. Working from the premise that no lyric poet had been 'as much talked about and as often misunderstood as Robert Burns', it was Daiches who first set out in the middle of last century to rescue the poet from the 'mists of sentimental oratory' of the Burns Supper tradition and to restore him to his 'significance as Scottish poet and literary craftsman.' And subsequent Burns scholarship owes much to Daiches' pioneering re-evaluation and re-assessment.

Crawford asserts that 'Burns *was* in several ways the first of the English-speaking world's great Romantic poets' and 'the first great Romantic poet to write about America'. Crawford is able to draw from previously untapped sources, particularly the MacDonald manuscript, a contemporary document of some of Burns' last conversations, and is the first biographer to mention the correspondence that Burns had with Mary Wollstonecraft, although no letters from either side seem to have survived. While Crawford's biography does succeed in avoiding 'over-aestheticising Burns', and aims to 'show his political and well as his lyric imagination', it is Patrick Scott Hogg's *The Patriot Bard* that concentrates on Burns as 'the Poet Laureate of Democracy', presenting him as 'the major radical poet of the late Enlightenment period'. In relation to Burns' formative reading, Hogg discusses the hitherto underestimated importance of Masson's *Collection of English Prose and Verse* and the seminal influence that it was to have in shaping the radical values of the adult poet. Hogg also presents new material, in the form of two radical essays published anonymously in the 1790s, and which he ascribes to Burns. Like other recent attributions made by Hogg, these are likely to prove contentious to Burns scholars.

Ian McIntyre's *Robert Burns: a Life*, first published as *Dirt and Deity*, remains a readable biography. Though idiosyncratic, it nevertheless appears as a staple on many university undergraduate course reading lists. While this speaks of the worth of McIntyre's work as a valuable background text, with the publication of these other two biographies, one wonders how long it will be before it is displaced.

Paradoxically, towards the end of his biography, Robert Crawford points to the danger of forgetting that 'Scotland's greatest poet belongs to the art form of poetry, not as an adjunct to or excuse for tourism, "creative industries", rock concerts or marketeers' gigs.' Though Scotland's manufacturing base has all but vanished, in this year of the Scottish Government's 'Homecoming' initiative, the country boasts a thriving Burns industry, for which Queen's Awards may well be made to various publishers. In addition to his massive biography, Crawford has also edited *New Poems, Chiefly in the Scottish Dialect,* a collection of offerings by contemporary poets that takes a 'sly wink at the master', and with Christopher MacLachlan, *The Best Laid Schemes,* a selection of Burns' poems and prose, both published by Polygon. Another anniversary offering of note comes from the Sandstone Press: *Fickle Man: Robert Burns in the 21st Century*, eighteen bold and challenging essays, edited by Johnny Rodger and Gerald Carruthers. Who says that Scottish publishing is in the doldrums?

Michael Lister

Nature Over Again: The Garden Art of Ian Hamilton Finlay
John Dixon Hunt. Reaktion Books. ISBN 9781861893932. £29.95

This well-illustrated and enjoyable essay is a welcome addition to the literature on Ian Hamilton Finlay, and is the first significant publication about his work since his death in 2006. Its title refers to the quotation from Cézanne to 'do Poussin over again after nature', that Finlay inverted as 'Nature over again after Poussin', and is thus a reference to a remaking of a proposed remaking: appropriate to the layered interrogation of culture that was Finlay's hallmark. It is, however, curious, that on p.169, Finlay's version of these words seems to be confused with Cézanne's. The emphasis of the book is the importance of the garden for Ian Hamilton Finlay, not just his own, extraordinary, garden of Little Sparta, at Dunsyre on the slopes of the Pentland Hills near Edinburgh, but also his significant international contributions.

This focus on Finlay as a maker of gardens is relevant and welcome, not least because it brings to attention work such as the garden designed at Fleur de l'Air in Provence, which has received relatively little notice. I would, however have welcomed more treatment of the Scottish context of Finlay's work. There is, for example, only marginal discussion of Little Sparta as Finlay's poetical and philosophical riposte to Edinburgh as 'the Athens of the North'. To sidestep Scotland as a driver of neo-classicism misses a trick for me. But perhaps the more important point is that this extended essay – by drawing attention to a great many of the issues with which Finlay engaged in his intellectually exploratory art of gardens – also helps to create agendas for further thinking about his work.

Finlay's work is a kind of selective cultural index in its own right (sometimes it puts me in mind of Patrick Geddes' project for an *Encyclopaedia Graphica*), and I was disappointed by the absence of an index and by the lack of editorial control and proof-reading in the notes. One unfortunate example is the repeated reference to Alec Finlay as 'Alex'; this occurs in the context of mentioning his editing of *Wood Notes Wild*, a notable essay collection about his father's work, referred to frequently in the notes, in one of which both 'Alec' and 'Alex' occur, an error that should have been picked up. I hope it will be in subsequent editions.

Murdo Macdonald

New Perspectives on the Irish in Scotland
Ed. Martin J. Mitchell. John Donald. ISBN 9781904607830. £20.00

These twelve essays consider the impact that immigration from Ireland has had on Scottish society from the entire nineteenth century to the second world war. Individual chapter titles give some idea of the scope of the collection. These include: 'The Great Irish Famine and Scottish History' by T.M. Devine; 'Irish Migrants in the Scottish Episcopal Church in the Nineteenth Century' by Ian Meredith; 'A Winnowing Spirit: Sinn Féin in Scotland, 1905–38' by Máirtín Ó Catháin; 'Our Country's Heroes: Irish Catholics in Scotland and the Great War' by Elaine W. McFarland; and 'Protestant Action and the Edinburgh Irish' by Michael Rosie. The collection's unifying concern is to understand the issues raised within a wider Scottish context. The contributors examine developments in Scotland that resulted from Irish immigration; the reactions among Scots, official and otherwise, to successive waves of migrants; and the lives of certain immigrant workers, businessmen, politicians and clergy in the Scottish communities in which they lived. They do not, however, deal with the immigrants' experiences in isolation.

Other chapters do not restrict themselves to a single identifiable historical episode, like those mentioned above, but rather focus on wider social issues such as institutional sectarianism or residential segregation, with several contributors undertaking local case studies in order to draw conclusions. John Foster, Muir Houston and Chris Madigan contribute a study of two Clydeside communities (Govan and Kinning Park) in the late nineteenth century, using Census reports to inform their detailed analysis. They find that segregation between Catholic and Protestant immigrants from Ulster, although intense at first, was negligible by 1901, while in Belfast, among those who did not emigrate, it grew far more intense during the same period. To explain these diverging trends, the authors highlight the non-sectarian and effective labour organisation that dominated Clydeside politics in the late nineteenth century. Geraldine Vaughan's chapter on local politics in Monklands draws on the author's research in letters, demonstrating that Irish Catholics who achieved local office or business success in this area were often held in high regard by the community at large.

Most of the contributors reflect briefly on existing scholarship and locate their findings in opposition to this work. Foster, Houston and Madigan note among earlier histories, 'an unhistorical tendency to treat Irish immigrants as socially isolated and, often in consequence, to assume them to be demographically homogeneous and culturally unchanging.' Editor Martin J. Mitchell agrees and illustrates the point with reference to the work of writers including Michael Fry, David McCrone, Christopher Harvie, Tom Gallagher, Callum Brown and William Walker. By contrast, since this collection takes Scotland as a whole, and because immigrant or host population behaviours are each tested for their effects upon the other, the whole process of immigration is understood as one of relationship and interdependence, situated within a wider national context. The collection therefore largely succeeds in its offer to view immigration from Ireland to Scotland from a fresh standpoint.

There are two slight inconsistencies. Bernard Aspinwall's essay 'Catholic Devotion in Victorian Scotland' examines developments in the Scottish Catholic Church at a time of significant Irish immigration, and thus agrees with the overall emphasis on immigration as a process of relationship. However, the author voices his apparently strong personal preferences. There is an open bias towards social conservativism and the essay tends to dismiss the church's 'large, low-wage, unskilled base' while it praises individual wealthy benefactors and the clergy. It also seems to lament the twentieth century decline of 'the power and wealth of the Catholic aristocracy [and] their influence within the church'. 'Vatican II, affluence and education,' writes Aspinwall, 'destroyed worthy regimentation that served in the darkest days.' Meanwhile, marriages between Catholics and Protestants are described at first as 'mixed' but later as 'irregular'. All of this might represent an attempt to reflect a certain Victorian worldview to the reader, but it is presented uncritically and therefore as the author's own stance.

In addition, editorial standards have not been consistently applied, so that while most chapters are error-free, standards falter in other places. Fortunately, the main undertaking is securely achieved. T.M. Devine contributes a second essay, entitled 'The End of Disadvantage?', which analyses the social and political changes that have occurred in Scotland since 1945, partly as a result of Irish Catholic immigration. Like the other writers, Devine is willing to recognise the communal and integrated picture that, to a large extent, is the legacy of Irish immigration to Scotland (notwithstanding the existence of certain tensions, of course). From this standpoint, this collection is able to convey, and in some cases begin to measure precisely, the extent of the role that immigration from Ireland has played in shaping modern Scotland.

Alasdair Gillon

Contemporary Scottish Literature: A Reader's Guide to Essential Criticism
Matt McGuire. Palgrave Macmillan. ISBN 9780230506701. £13.99

One of a series of texts published by Palgrave to provide a 'starting point and easy access to the essential criticism on key authors and genres of world literature', this work provides a lucid and detailed examination of critical trends surrounding Scottish fiction from the publication of Alasdair Gray's groundbreaking *Lanark* (1981) to the present.

As McGuire points out, 'the politics of national identity have exerted a disproportionate influence on the critical imagination in Scotland'. He seeks to explore 'the alternative questions that have come to preoccupy the Scottish imagination in recent decades'. In this, he is undoubtedly successful. In six core chapters, he outlines crucial issues in contemporary Scottish writing: nation and nationalism; language; gender; class; postcolonialism; and postmodernism. Embracing theoretical positions that have come to inform literary scholarship in Scotland since the late 1980s, McGuire is an able guide with a formidable grasp of his subject. He is comprehensive in his references to key texts and articles which have extended the possibilities for discussing Scottish literature over the past twenty years.

It is a particular strength that critical issues are seen in practice. Each chapter ends with a detailed examination of particular writers in whose work key themes or issues can be seen manifested. In his chapter on class, for example, McGuire explores the work of James Kelman, while the chapter on postmodernism includes a survey of work by Muriel Spark and A.L. Kennedy.

Aimed largely at an undergraduate audience, McGuire's book is pitched exactly right. He does not attempt to water down the complexities involved in competing political and cultural forms of nationalism, for example; nor does he attempt to evade the problematic use of postcolonial theory to account for certain features of Scottish writing. On the other hand, he is always conscious of his audience, explaining his terms as he goes: from metonymy to ontology, glosses are provided. *Contemporary Scottish Literature* represents how far Scottish literature and its criticism have come in the past two decades, eschewing essentialist notions of 'Scotland' or 'Scottishness' in favour of more inclusive perspectives.

David Borthwick

The Blasphemies of Thomas Aikenhead: Boundaries of Belief on the Eve of the Enlightenment
Michael F. Graham. EUP. ISBN 9780748634262. £50.00

I admit a personal interest in this case. If my aunt's genealogical search is reliable, I am related to an unfortunate, short-lived blasphemer. In 1697, Thomas Aikenhead was the last person to be hanged in Scotland for blasphemy. An orphan, twenty at most, Aikenhead used his 'tender years' as part of his appeal against his sentence. His was a first offence, yet the law stated that capital punishment for blasphemy should only be instigated for a third offence. His sentence rested on the testimony of fellow students, in particular Mungo Craig, whom Aikenhead claimed had supplied him with literature which prompted his 'cursing and railling'. He begged forgiveness, requested reprieve in which to make his peace with God. The church had the opportunity to intervene on his behalf. It didn't. Graham shows how demographics and topology contributed to Edinburgh's close-knit, high-density community. He shows how hard the times were. The harvests failed two years in a row. People starved. In anticipation of a French invasion, armies were mustered. Plague broke out. Political and religious loyalties were volatile. The Privy Council ordered a purge on bookshops which stocked deist or atheistic material and there was Aikenhead, casting doubt on the scriptures.

A question for any historian is how to provide contextual overview while maintaining subject focus. When Graham goes in close, he brings Aikenhead's world to life. When he takes us on a whirlwind skim of the seventeenth century, he loses me. The large cast becomes unwieldy at times; we don't need to hear twice, for example, that 'Carstares... had been tortured with thumbscrews in 1684 for his suspected knowledge of the Rye House Plot.' Phrases like 'ongoing hard-core Presbyterian refusal', 'political circus' and summarising platitudes detract from the authority of the text.

The parallel drawn between Aikenhead and the young Spinoza, (excommunicated in 1656 from his Jewish community), emphasises the perils of being in the wrong place at the wrong time, but the more interesting proposition – that Aikenhead might also have had philosophical worth – is summarily dismissed. Aikenhead's execution is considered a milestone on Scotland's dark road to the Enlightenment and Graham shows us with vividness and some effective dramatic timing, the worst that can happen when self-righteousness and political expediency join forces.

Dilys Rose

The Bird Room
Chris Killen. Canongate Books. ISBN 9781847672605. £9.99

The Bird Room, Killen's debut novel, cannot be called enjoyable. From the first words – presenting our nude narrator, genitals adorned with a hat – it is intent on conveying a strong sense of the wrongness present in the world, and executes this with aplomb. The writing is often clever and incisive but also sloppy, with the cleverness occasionally feeling contrived. The result is compelling but slick, and it left me dissatisfied.

At the book's core lies a self-conscious, disordered descent through our narrator Will's tortured psyche, intertwined with the tangential tale of Helen (aka Clair), also struggling to find her way. The structure is tidy and produces the desired effect of shrouding certain aspects of the story in mystery, while sharpening the focus on the hedonistic impulses of the main characters and those around them. The two stories are undeniably fascinating, with the appeal of all disasters – sensationalised plots of two lives spiralling out of control offer up plenty of misery at which to gawk.

Killen makes liberal use of a bit of postmodern flair (think Dave Eggers), inserting a checklist, a connect-the-dots, and several items of e-correspondence into his text. Although on principle I have no objections to such devices, some are less successfully employed than others. In places these tricks are distracting and clumsy – such as the awkward time-skip near the start of the novel (between the front door of the second Will's apartment and his sofa) or the exact repetition of three lines of dialogue (from the mouths of two different characters) when the two Wills meet for a drink with Will the artist's impressionable Eastern European friend. There is a sense that the writing is strong enough to do without some of these affectations, although Killen can be forgiven for bending to the temptation of adding a few unnecessary whistles and bells in his first novel.

Underneath its postmodern sheen, *The Bird Room* toys with some interesting ideas about identity and our flawed modern society. The ploy of giving the same name to the protagonist and his tormentor-in-chief is obvious but expertly utilised, and Alice and Helen's overlapping transformations are skillfully executed. As if sharing a name is not enough, Will the lesser and Will the greater also share strange obsessions with pornography and similar degrees of cluelessness about how and why the world around them functions as it does. The boundaries which so blatantly separate the successful young artist (in bloom) from his pathetic, paranoid, erstwhile friend become painfully blurred at times. The best example is the most sensationalised moment in the novel – when Will the narrator's girlfriend Alice makes love to Will the painter in their own flat as he watches on. However, Killen also extends more subtle invitations into the grey areas of modern morality, as when Will the painter proposes to manufacture an art exhibit from a relationship:

'I'm going to hire some girl to have a relationship with me and then break up with her and exhibit it all. I'll take photos and video and audio of everything. Absolutely everything. So when you go into the gallery, it'll be like really uncomfortable and you'll wonder how much of this stuff you should be seeing.'

And yet at the end of the book, it is Will the narrator who pays Helen to have sex with him whilst being filmed. But can we be sure? When introducing himself to Helen, he blurs the boundaries further: 'I'm William,' he says. 'Or Will.'

The author's talent is evident, but at times Killen allows his own cleverness to run away with him, leaving partially explored ideas littered behind. He amuses himself with the concept of Will (the narrator) interacting with the world as if it is a computer, double-clicking on Alice and selecting and deleting Will (the painter). This life-through-the-computer-screen motif is echoed in places – the intrusion of links to porn sites into a conversation between the two Wills, and the graphic e-mail responses to Helen's online profile – but isn't followed through in any meaningful way. Similarly, the ending leaves nothing resolved, save that Alice has left Will (the narrator), presumably for a relationship with Will (the painter). This lack of 'closure' is surely intentional, given that the novel makes no claims to be conventional, and seems to aim at maximising the reader's discomfort.

Andy Gloege

Twinset
Poems by Karen Knight and Dilys Rose. Illustrations by Laurie Hastings and Polly Thelwall. Knucker Press. ISBN 9780955501357. www.knuckerpress.com. £7.00
Quarry
Dawn Wood. Templar Poetry. ISBN 9781906285081. £9.99
Adrift/Napospas vlnám
Ian Stephen. Periplum with the British Council. ISBN 9788086624358. www.periplam.cz. €7.40
Late Love & Other Whodunnits
Diana Hendry. Peterloo Poets and Mariscat Press. ISBN 9780946588480. £7.95

Being myself unable to comprehend how artistic collaborations are feasible – how that most territorial of creatures, the poet, becomes willing to give up ground to another – I am further amazed by how such a project then coalesces into a readable whole. Whether it is by serendipity or pure design, *Twinset*, the collaboration between Tasmanian poet Karen Knight and Scottish poet Dilys Rose, is unfailingly surprising in all the right ways.

In *Twinset*, Knight and Rose have each written poems towards a shared topic. At times, the results are remarkably similar, a common nerve apparently having been struck, almost as if both poems had arisen from the same consciousness. The collaboration most excels, however, in the places where conceptions diverge. The best examples of this are in the poems written upon the theme of 'the sun', which Rose's poem treats as an heirloom plate first acquired before the outset of World War II, then reconceptualises as Japan's Rising Sun. In Knight's poem, the Sun Man arrives, selling from a briefcase: 'His spiel was flawless./ He sold me a summer/ without any shade./ I felt his subcutaneous sting.' Both are absolutely distinctive in their conceptions and their voicings.

Of course each of these poets, accomplished in her own right, is stylistically distinctive as well. Rose's work is hallmarked by its colloquial turns and a grounding in dramatic scene, while Knight's is recognisable by its steadily contrived and delivered lyric, such that the poems in the collection move from a conversational to an internalised voice and back again. In the discourse between these two poets' sensibilities, the sensation of the poems moving towards each other and then apart, they have produced a body of work that manages to be, somehow, greater than the sum of its parts.

The debut collection from Dawn Wood, *Quarry*, reflects the hunt that preoccupies the first few poems of the book: perplexing, frustrating, requiring of patience. In these opening pages, Wood is given frequently to a meandering rhetoric, a habit of suspending words or clauses that confounds her reader with an overly complicated sentence (sometimes syntactically nebulous) and undermining the impacts made by individual lines.

On the other hand, it is evident Wood has the skill to craft the precise line or evocative image when she writes, 'I am frugal, I have saved/ few objects – the fragments of a mirror;/ a book to swear on.' Likewise, the internal half-rhyming in 'Nearing Midsummer, Highland Perthshire' of combinations of words ('amazed as usual' with 'unmistakable' with 'once invisible') is drastically at odds with the writer that allows, as a description of movement, 'slightly hypnotically lumpily', without so much as an intervening comma.

This un-evenness persists throughout the first half of the book, until one reaches the section titled 'The Herd Book of Sonnets.' I would not so much hesitate to call these sonnets as I would be quick to call them otherwise: only a length of fourteen lines appears to recommend them as such. Nonetheless, this section of the book is where Wood begins to put her talents on display. Her lines are syntactically careful, and markedly more musical than most of those seen early on.

The book moves back into Wood's more rhetorical style, but maintains the sort of compelling statement and line-management of the 'sonnets'. Barring the inconsistencies, *Quarry* is musical, moving, and ultimately enjoyable.

Adrift offers a cross-section of Ian Stephen's nearly three decades' worth of poetic and dramatic work. His poetry is dynamic and succinct, to the point where I have been tempted to reproduce, here, poems in their entireties. His work has its spiritual home in the Hebrides and their surrounding waters. For Stephen, the sea and shore are vibrant, active; landscape is not background, it is interwoven with the author's own personality. Stephen expresses himself in terms alternately flowing and lyrical, or imagistic and disaffected. He deals as readily with questions of aesthetic as he does with the grimy trivialities of the everyday. The result is, either way, voiced with economy and pathos.

Whether enacting a muted engagement with natural beauty, or employing the common idiom, this is a poet attuned to the old injunction to 'Know Thyself', or as he might admit with less ceremony, 'I bide within limited parallels,/ shuffle a few meridians.'

It is hard to look at the cover of *Late Love & Other Whodunnits* and not be impressed by its cosiness: the two-toned blue of it, the heart-shaped depiction of a man and a woman in bed. The opening poems feel no less cosy, the verse affected by an unimposing but noticeable music, typified by these lines from 'You, Going Away': 'I could stay/ in the Hall of Departures called home,/ wash the plate you ate from,/ fold the clothes you left behind/ or come to the station.' Poetry of this kind – on those timeless themes of love and loss – will always risk the charge of being sentimental. Hendry appears to have been aware enough of the danger to mitigate the outcome.

While at first glance it might seem otherwise, *Late Love...* does not deal solely in romance and maternal devotions. Included in the collection is a series of psalm translations and responses previously published in pamphlet form. Unfortunately, the translations are not particularly inspiring: they carry epigrams, though the poems themselves seem only pertinent as epigrams to the subsequent response pieces. The rewritings are interesting re-contextualisations, which would probably have succeeded without the attendant paraphrased psalm.

Structurally, the artifice of the psalms and responses interrupts the pervasive sincerity upon which the rest of this collection relies. This amounts to a minor mis-step; there follows the collection's most compelling work, a series of elegies, each of which (and a number of poems elsewhere) isolates a single line following the final stanza – for me, a too-obvious device that begs to be read as poignancy. Still, by and large, Hendry takes adroit risks with her material.

Stephen Lackaye

An Honest Trade: Booksellers and Bookselling in Scotland
Eds. Alistair McCleery, David Finkelstein, and Jennie Renton. ISBN
9780859766739. £7.99

A decade ago, Scotland was home to a number of well-established, family-owned bookshops staffed with people knowledgeable about their goods and their customers' needs. Today, few survive, and this book charts this dramatic change in Scottish bookselling through interviews with the last practitioners.

The collapse of the Net Book Agreement in the mid 1990s, by which publishers set the price of books, contributed greatly to this state of affairs. The same book could now be sold at different prices and Scottish booksellers who, throughout the twentieth century, had built relatively secure businesses upon the certain value of their stock, were now thrown into a world where Tesco, Borders, or Amazon could afford to sell more books for far less than they. According to Hugh Andrew, who wrote the Foreword, this environment created a 'monopoly' that gave great advantage to the 'corporate giants' over a diverse, venerated, and well-established community of wholesalers, library suppliers, and bookshops.

But not all interviewees are in agreement. According to Willie Anderson of John Smith & Sons, booksellers were too complacent and slow to adapt to a changing market: 'I think the most telling example of it was the case of the book tokens. We spent our lives licking the damn things to stick them onto cards, which we then had the temerity to ask the customer to pay for. This was not actually a customer-friendly thing.'

Many of the interviews are like this: open, candid, and reflective not only about why so many bookshops closed after so long a history, but also what the day-to-day life in a bookshop was like. We hear of bookfolk that could appear in a Dickens novel: 'a very ancient bookseller who operated... with a camp bed in his shop and a pistol under his pillow'. One would like to think that scholar-thieves who wanted to read at three in the morning would be given a book rather than a mortal wound. Reading these stories, one feels as if they are being regaled in a pub by a chap with a pint, a pipe, and a worthy tale. The memoirs have an important contribution to make to the history of Scottish bookselling, and scholars and readers will be grateful that the stories were collected while they could still be told.

Ross Alloway

The Rotten State of Britain: Who is causing the crisis and how to solve it
Eamonn Butler. Gibson Square Books Ltd. ISBN 9781906142346. £12.99

And another thing. Christmas parties. Do you know that they have to put nut warnings now on mince pies? Can't serve a glass of wine without a permit. Or sing carols without an entertainment licence. Just don't get me started – dodgy A levels, community support officers, sale of honours, the Millenium Dome, wind farms, clostridium difficile. Country's going to hell in a handcart. I had that Enoch Powell in the back of the institute back in the 1980s. Proper gent he was.

Eamonn Butler's critique of New Labour sometimes reads like a 300-page editorial from the *Daily Mail*. However, he isn't all wrong by any means, even if he never knowingly understates his case. Like Spinal Tap, Butler keeps the volume turned up to 11: 'We were promised Cool Britannia, a People's Government', he says of Tony Blair's 1997 agenda, 'but instead we got boom and bust, injustice, surveillance, regulation, stealth taxes, interference, sleaze, lies, hoodies and binge-drinking ladettes'. So, not all bad then...

The Rotten State of Britain is intended to be an answer to Will Hutton's *The State We're In* which helped prepare the ground for Labour's election victory in 1997. Butler lacks Hutton's easy erudition, his measured humanity. This is not so much a broadside as an all-out assault on land and sea, with no prisoners and no quarter. But the curious thing is that, as a fully paid up member of the liberal left, I found myself disagreeing with very little of Butler's inventory of ignominy.

New Labour has indeed been a disaster, on so many fronts. Tony Blair spun us into an illegal war in Iraq, on the basis of ludicrous claims that Saddam Hussein had weapons of mass destruction which could hit British targets within 45 minutes. And when it was found out, the government reacted by emasculating the BBC and driving the weapons inspector, Dr David Kelly – a decent man, if not entirely blameless – to suicide. Tens of thousands of Iraqis, four thousand American servicemen and two hundred British soldiers joined Kelly in paying the ultimate price for this reckless folly.

Butler is strongest when he deals with how Labour used the 'war on terror' to mount an assault on our historic liberties. *Habeas corpus*, freedom of speech, jury trials and the right to privacy have been invaded by officialdom in the pursuit of the terrorist chimera. Anti-terrorism legislation has not only been used against Icelandic banks, but also against people who demonstrate within a mile of Parliament, heckle ministers at Labour conference, or wear a 'Bollocks to Blair' tee-shirt. Suspects can be held without charge for four weeks – and it was only the House of Lords that prevented it turning into 90 days. Britain now has a quarter of the world's CCTV cameras.

Tony Blair promised Labour would be 'whiter than white, purer than pure'. But this government has corrupted parliamentary democracy in a way the Tories would never have got away with. Number 10 handed honours to millionaires in exchange for large donations which it sought to disguise as loans to prevent public disclosure. But it is on the economy that Labour has really fallen down. Gordon Brown promised an end to boom and bust; he delivered an epic boom followed by a catastrophic bust. Britain now has a trillion pound public debt. And as Butler rightly points out, this is before you take into account the cost of bank rescues, unfunded public sector pensions, the decommissioning of nuclear power stations and the overhang of PFI. The government that promised full employment will soon preside over three million unemployed.

Yes, I know, I'm beginning to sound a bit like Butler. But it's hard not to froth just a little at the mouth when reviewing the last ten years. It is no accident that this book could not find a publisher when it was first written in 2007. Since then the economic crisis 'which began in America' has undermined support for Labour to such an extent that a Tory polemic has clearly become marketable once more. Butler hardly mentions David Cameron, but his prescriptions for Rotten Britain make it pretty clear where he is coming from. I don't myself see how yet more privatisation can solve the economic problems caused by three decades of deregulation; how private health and education would be an improvement; or how Wisconsin-style workfare can be imposed in an era of mass unemployment.

Butler's loathing of New Labour blinds him to its modest achievements. The NHS is better funded and performance is improved, as is the state of school buildings and the state of nursery provision. Tax credits may be infuriatingly complex, but they have made work pay. There have been constitutional changes like devolution which have improved democratic accountability. However, the balance-sheet is undoubtedly negative. Sometimes governments behave so badly that they simply don't deserve to be re-elected, even if the opposition don't have all the answers. This is indeed a damning indictment and one which is likely to appeal to more than just the angry mob who read the *Daily Mail*.

Iain Macwhirter

Notes on Contributors

Hannah Adcock is a graduate of Cambridge University and freelance writer who has been commissioned to write articles for both the national and regional press. Her first book, *Twentysomething: The Ultimate Survival Guide* (Discover Press, 2004) was published when she was twenty-three.

Uilleam Blacker was born in Glasgow, grew up on the Isle of Barra and now lives in London. He is writing his PhD thesis on Ukrainian literature, which he also translates. He has lived in Ukraine, Poland and Russia, and writes academically on the literatures of all these countries.

Will Brady grew up near the south coast of England. He studied Literature and Fine Art and is currently based in Edinburgh, where he works as a freelance graphic designer, photographer and writer.

Regi Claire was born and brought up in Switzerland. Her first two books are *Inside-Outside* and *The Beauty Room*. She has been awarded several prizes and bursaries for her work. *Fighting It*, a collection of short stories, is due to be published this summer.

Catherine Czerkawska has written poems, novels, short stories and plays including *Wormwood*, about the Chernobyl disaster, for the Traverse Theatre, *The Price of a Fish Supper* and *Burns on the Solway* for the Oran Mor, in Glasgow.

Robin Gillanders is Reader in Photography at Edinburgh Napier University. He has exhibited extensively and his previous books include *The Philosopher's Garden*, (National Galleries of Scotland, 2004); *The Photographic Portrait* (David & Charles, 2004) and *Little Sparta* (National Galleries of Scotland, 1998).

Andrew Greig was born in Bannockburn, and grew up in Anstruther, Fife. He has published several books of poetry, most recently *This Life, This Life: New and Selected Poems 1970–2006* (Bloodaxe, 2006) and five novels, most recently *Romanno Bridge* (Quercus, 2008).

Jen Hadfield's first collection, Almanacs (2005), and her second collection, Nigh No Place (2008) are both published by Bloodaxe. She received an Eric Gregory Award in 2003, which she used to fund a year in Canada. She is the 2008 winner of the T.S. Eliot Prize.

Fred Johnston received a Hennessy Literary Award for prose in 1972. Since then he has published eight volumes of poetry, a collection of stories and three novels. His most recent collection is *The Oracle Room* (Cinnamon Poetry).

James Kelman writes stories and lives in Glasgow.

Kenny Kemp is an author and business journalist based in Edinburgh. He was a Business Editor of *The Scotsman* and founding Business Editor of the *Sunday Herald*.

Dorothy Lawrenson is a painter and graphic designer. She was born in Dundee and studied Fine Art at Edinburgh University and Edinburgh College of Art. Her debut pamphlet, *Under the Threshold,* was shortlisted for a Callum Macdonald Memorial Award.

Tom Leonard's first publication, *Six Glasgow Poems,* appeared in 1969. His latest, *Outside the Narrative: New and Selected Poems* is due from Etruscan Books this summer. There is a selection of critical and political prose, together with some poetry, on his website, www.tomleonard.co.uk.

Robyn Marsack is the Director of the Scottish Poetry Library.

Ian McDonough is originally from Sutherland. His sequence *A Rising Fever* was published by Kettilonia in 2000: that year he produced a series of poems on particle physics for the Engineering and Science Research Council. His first full collection, *Clan MacHine*, was shortlisted for Scottish First Book of the Year in 2004. His most recent collection is *The Vanishing Hitchhiker* (Mariscat).

Bernard Pearson was born in Cirencester in 1955. He now lives in Newport, South Wales with his wife and two children.

Ross Wilson, a national schoolboy boxing champion and Scottish internationalist, boxed for Rosyth ABC. A Hawthornden Fellow in 2004, his work has appeared in *New Writing Scotland*, *Northwords*, *Agenda Broadsheets*, *Horizon Review*, *Markings*, *Poetry Scotland*, and the *Macallan Shorts* (Polygon) Website: www.wetlink.wetpaint.com.

Acknowledgements

'Scots Pine' by Andrew Greig is excerpted from *At the Loch of the Green Corrie,* the story of a fishing mission to Assynt at the request of Norman MacCaig – in part biography, personal memoir, meditation on fishing, writing, geology, land ownership, whisky, friendship, Scotland, transience and generally being human. It will be published by Quercus in spring 2009.

'Russian Blue' is from *Fighting It,* a new collection of stories by Regi Claire, to be published by Two Ravens Press in June 2009.